# Starting with Bantams

## David Scrivener

## Broad Leys Publishing Ltd

**Starting with Bantams**

First published: 2002

Copyright © 2002 David Scrivener

Editor: Katie Thear
Published by Broad Leys Publishing Ltd

A catalogue record for this book is available from the British Library.

ISBN: 0 906137 31 4

Outside front cover: Dutch bantam (John Tarren)

Outside Back Cover: Group of garden bantams (Katie Thear)
                    Photo of the author (John Tarren)

The publishers are grateful to the following bantam breeders for permission to photograph their birds:
    Stuart Morton. Tel: 01279 777001
    Tawny Bantams & Miniatures. Tel: 01787 282096
    The Domestic Fowl Trust Tel: 01386 833083
    West Gate Bantams. Tel: 01787 312492

For details of other publications please contact the publishers:
Broad Leys Publishing Ltd
1 Tenterfields,
Newport, Saffron Walden,
Essex CB11 3UW.
Tel/Fax: 01799 541065
E-mail: info@blpbooks.co.uk
Website: www.blpbooks.co.uk

# Contents

# Introduction

*By art likewise we make them greater or smaller than their kind is and contrariwise dwarf them and stay their growth.* (Francis Bacon, 1629)

Most people start keeping hens in their garden to have fresh eggs from happy hens. These are usually commercial hybrids, with perhaps, some pure breed hens, often dark brown egg-laying Marans or Welsummers, or possibly blue or green egg laying Araucanas.

As interest in poultry develops, many start thinking about breeding some birds, especially if they have visited a farm park or poultry show and seen for themselves something of the incredible range of shapes, sizes and colours in which chickens have been developed.

Crowing cockerels are a worry for many for they are a recognised 'noise nuisance' in law. If you become a breeder, and that means cockerels, will the neighbours complain? Probably, yes, if they are close neighbours, unless action is taken to lessen the noise. In fact, there are many breeders in our towns and cities. Cocks can be kept shut in their houses, which muffles the noise, until after everyone is up and about, and some breeds, such as Ko-Shamo and Dutch, are quieter than others. The noisy road, railway line or airport you have hitherto cursed is now welcome camouflage.

With so many kinds to choose from, and space being limited for most of us, many hobbyist breeders keep bantams instead of the full sized breeds. *True bantams* are chickens that are naturally small, and which have no larger counterparts. Miniature versions of many breeds of large fowl have also been produced. Two or three varieties of bantams can be kept in the space needed for one large fowl flock. Many beginners start with several breeds, a sensible first move to find out quickly, at first hand, what they are really like.

The *Breeds* section of this book includes guidance on which breeds are suitable for beginners, and which are best left for a few years, until more experience is gained. The sensible second move, over the next two or three years, is to cut down to fewer breeds, with more birds of each type. Some people end up with several colour varieties of one breed, or the full sized and bantam versions of the same breed, the equivalent of a dog breeder with *Standard* and *Toy* Poodles.

In the 1950s, when commercial poultry farming changed from using pure breeds to hybrids, many historic breeds nearly became extinct. They were only kept going by poultry show exhibitors, and even the shows had a lean time from 1945 to 1965, but from the late 1960s interest picked up, and almost all of the old breeds have survived, although some are still very rare. So, by breeding good quality pure breeds, hopefully for many years, you can have a valuable conservation centre in your back garden.

Crowing cockerels are regarded as a 'noise nuisance' in law. Keeping them in their house until later in the morning helps to muffle the sound.

One unfortunate reason for people giving up our hobby is letting their enthusiasm run amok. They end up with far too many birds, of too many kinds. The sensible ones happily keep their chosen favourites for a lifetime.

The annual cycle from setting eggs in an incubator or under a broody, anticipating the arrival of those cute fluffy chicks, and then watching them gradually develop into (one hopes) fine examples of their breed, ready to produce the next generation, is a fascinating process.

This book is called *Starting with Bantams*, and should guide you through the first few years of the hobby. Hopefully you will read others to expand your knowledge.

Most of the ideas here also apply to large fowl pure breeds, especially the more exotic kinds. It is just a question of increasing the sizes of the houses to suit.

*(David Scrivener, 2002)*

The Friesian, classified as a large, light breed, is probably typical of a medieval hen. (Katie Thear)

Large fowl and true bantam (both females but obviously not of the same breed) showing the relative difference in size. (Katie Thear)

# History of bantams

The fowls kept in Europe until about 1500 were generally of the size and shape we now define as *Large Light Breeds*. Most would have weighed between 1½ and 2½ kg. The Friesian, a Dutch breed now bred here in small numbers, is probably fairly typical of a medieval hen.

A few European explorers had reached Asia centuries before, but significant contact and trade really began with the Portugese fleet led by Vasco da Gama. The Portugese set up a chain of trading posts from East Africa, via India, to the islands of South East Asia. Included was one at Bantam on the western end of Java, established in 1522. Among the exotic spices and silks brought back to Europe were an assortment of tiny chickens, which would eventually be developed into the 400+ varieties known today. These miniature fowls probably came from other places apart from Bantam, so perhaps the Dutch, French and Germans are more realistic in their words *Kriel*, *Nain* and *Zwerg*, all of which simply mean dwarf, as their general terms for these birds.

Organised poultry shows and formal breed standards, as we know them today, began about 1850. Consequently most bantam breeds were developed after then, but a few were established long before. The oldest bantam breed is probably the Black Rosecomb. King Richard III was recorded as admiring a flock of them when staying at The Angel Inn, Grantham, Lincolnshire in 1483. How they got to Lincolnshire at such an early date is unknown, although one clue is in their original name, Black Africans. Perhaps Arab traders brought them from South East Asia to East Africa, and they came to Europe from there.

Black Rosecomb Bantams are not quite, but very nearly, miniatures of large Black Hamburghs, an ancient breed widely bred in Northern England and what is now Holland and Germany, for centuries. Bantams arrived in a range of shapes and colours. From them, the obvious direction to go for poultry breeders from the 16th century to the present day, was to select for miniature versions of the large breeds they already knew.

Cuckoo Bantams were popular in Scotland as they were a fair miniature representation of Scots Greys, the local farmyard breed. In England, where Game-cocks were the national favourite, the whole range of game colours could be reproduced on a small scale.

Bantams were not only taken to Europe for development into distinct breeds, but north too, to Japan. The breed called Japanese Bantam in Britain is called the Chabo in Japan and many other countries, derived from the old Japanese name for South East Asia and the Islands of Malaysia and Indonesia. They are very distinctive, with very short legs and long upright tails, and are clearly shown in Japanese paintings from 1603 onwards.

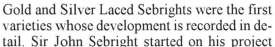

Above: Black Rosecombs. (Ludlow, 19th Century)
Right: White Rosecombs. (William Cook)

Gold and Silver Laced Sebrights were the first varieties whose development is recorded in detail. Sir John Sebright started on his project about 1800. Other breeders took up his new breed and the Sebright Bantam Club was formed in 1815, the first specialist breed club by a long way. They held an annual show at the Grey's Inn Coffee House on the first Tuesday in February. Maximum weights allowed were 22oz for cockerels and 18oz for pullets, and the main concentration was on perfecting the lacing.

As already said, poultry shows as we know them today began about 1850. The interest was clearly long established, but not until this time were there factories to produce show cages, and railways to get people and their birds to and from the shows. *The Poultry Club of Great Britain*, our governing body, was formed in 1877. From 1850 to 1939 the shows were mainly a shop window for commercial breeders and bantams were very much a minority interest. However, it was quite a large minority. Also, while a lot of the full sized breeds shown were from professional breeders - to advertise their stock to the then very high proportion of households who kept some hens in the garden - quite a few of the large breeds were more ornamental than practical.

W.F.Entwisle, of Wakefield, was a key person, as he created several miniature versions of already existing large breeds. After his death in 1892, both his son and daughter carried on to become important breeders in their own right. There were many other breeders doing the same thing, but the Entwisle family seem to have produced almost as many varieties as everyone else put together.

Since 1950 the shows have been very much a hobby, and bantams usually outnumber large fowl by a large margin, although in some southern counties there are nearly equal numbers of large fowl. Only a small proportion of poultry breeders have ever entered shows, but they have generally been the people with the best birds, and anyway, the shows have always been the only regular meeting places for those interested in poultry. Some people have criticised fanciers for neglecting the productive qualities of the birds, but without the shows to give a focus to breeders, many of our living heritage of old breeds would have died out long ago.

Scots Grey Bantam cock. Cuckoo Bantams were popular in Scotland as they were a fair miniature reproduction of Scots Greys, the local farmyard breed. The white tail feathers of this bird would be regarded as a fault at a show. (Katie Thear)

## Breed Standards

At the summer agricultural shows, judges are often asked by the curious public *"What are you looking for in a chicken?"* First they must be healthy, clean and preferably, reasonably tame. Most people are amazed to learn that many of the birds will have had a complete bath and pedicure. Then, they are told that each breed has a 'standard', or official description of an ideal specimen, and that the winners are the birds nearest to its ideal. In most cases it is then fairly obvious that the most important features are different for each breed. On some varieties it will be an intricate plumage pattern, on others, body shape or other physical features such as feathered feet or a very long tail.

This book can only give a brief outline of each breed. For full details you need *British Poultry Standards*. The current edition (1997) is 368 pages long and includes all varieties then recognised. Many of the standards have stood for over a century, but revisions are sometimes necessary and foreign breeds are sometimes imported to add to the range available here. Then, a translation of the standard used in the country of origin is adopted. The next edition is due in 2007.

Black-Tailed White Japanese Bantam hen and cockerel. (Katie Thear)

A breeding trio of Silver Sebrights in a movable house and run. (Katie Thear)

Completely new breeds are not likely to be accepted, but sometimes new colours of existing breeds, especially if they were known before but became extinct, are more welcome. White-crested Black Polands are popular. The reverse, Black-crested White Polands are in the process of being re-made by a group of European breeders. The original Black-crested Whites became extinct well over a century ago.

## Breed Groups

Poultry shows are divided into sections, just as dog shows are divided into *hound*, *terrier* and other groups. The bantam sections are:

| | |
|---|---|
| **Soft Feather Heavy Breeds** | **Rare Breeds** |
| **Soft Feather Light Breeds** | **True Bantams** |
| **Hard Feather Breeds** | |

The first four groups are miniature versions of large breeds, with *True Bantams* being bantam only types. (There is no large counterpart). The terms *Heavy* and *Light* are not entirely based on body weight; there is an element of body shape as well. Minorcas, the largest of the *Light Breeds*, are slightly heavier than the smaller *Heavy Breeds*, but are in the Light Breed group because they are closely related to Anconas and Leghorns in the same group. Such anomalies are more common in bantams than large fowl because some breeds have been miniaturised more than others. Barred Plymouth Rock bantams in the Heavy Breed section, are usually smaller than Minorca bantams. Do not confuse *Light*, meaning weight, with *Light*, meaning colour. Light Brahmas and Light Sussex are both colour varieties of Heavy Breeds

The old fighting-cock breeds belong in the *Hard Feather Large Fowl* group. After cock-fighting was banned in 1849 the Game-cock breeders turned to showing. Additional breeds in the same style, plus bantam versions of all of them were developed. As the group name suggests, they are less fluffy than Soft Feather breeds. Some look quite skinny, and even have patches of bare skin, especially along the breast bone. Do not be deceived by appearances! They are a lot heavier than they look, and the bare patches are perfectly alright, a legacy of some having originated from south-east Asia.

The definition of *Rare Breed* is not exactly related to numbers in existence, which is impossible to keep track of anyway. The breeds in the other sections have Breed Clubs, such as the Sussex Club, for breeders to join. Those breeds with not enough breeders in the UK to have such a club are all together in *The Rare Poultry Society*. Some breeds, such as Nankins and Spanish, are very rare worldwide. Others, such as German Langshans, are rare here but popular in other countries. If a Rare Breed becomes more popular, a club is formed, and that breed moves to the section to which it naturally belongs. Dutch (True) and New Hampshire Reds (Heavy) are both former Rare Breeds.

Some colour varieties of popular breeds are actually rarer than some of the designated Rare Breeds. Red Sussex and Brown Sussex are two examples, but they are still in the Heavy section along with the other more popular colours of Sussex.

# Points of a bantam

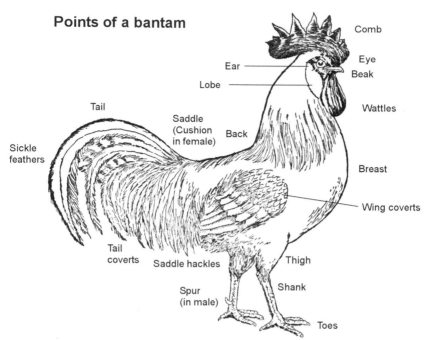

Comb

Eye

Beak

Ear

Lobe

Wattles

Tail

Saddle
(Cushion
in female)

Back

Sickle
feathers

Breast

Wing coverts

Tail
coverts

Saddle hackles

Thigh

Spur
(in male)

Shank

Toes

Various bantams illustrated by Ludlow in the 19th century. Top left: Frizzles. Top right: Golden Sebrights. Centre: Buff Pekins. Bottom left: Japanese. Bottom right: Spangled Old English Game.

# Getting started

*The day of small things should not be despised, as small beginnings often produce large endings.* (William Cook)

If bantams are to become a permanent part of the household, it is vital to think everything through before starting. Inevitably, some of the breeds or housing will prove to be bad ideas. Some logical thinking at the start might help to get more things right first time.

The main factors are the space and time available. Those living on a farm or smallholding will have room for good sized grassy runs, which will probably become muddy in winter. For this environment choose from the many breeds which will thrive in natural conditions, which is not all of them. Breeds with feathered feet, head crests or long tails and some others which need special care to keep them looking good, are best kept by breeders with more housing and less space, such as a tidy set-up in a suburban garden. The chapter on housing gives more details.

Remember that when you go on holiday, or even just away for a weekend, you will need to ask a neighbour or someone to feed and water the birds. This is not usually a problem, but it can be if you have a huge collection.

Of course, a lot of people will just want a single house and run, with just a few assorted bantam hens and no cockerel. They should remember that bantams may look sweet little things, but they can be vicious psychopaths to each other. It is safest to buy all the birds at once. Trying to add a new bird into a settled flock seldom works, unless a great deal of time and patience is spent. They need to be introduced, with a system of separate runs where they can see and get used to each other before being fully integrated. A newcomer will be bullied, possibly even killed by the others. Ideally choose bantams roughly all the same size, perhaps several different colour varieties of one breed.

Buying hens only can be difficult as all bantam breeders are just doing it as a hobby, and they do not want to be left with a load of cockerels and no hens to go with them. The best time to buy is late summer when the spring hatched chicks will be maturing and breeders are able to select those which they wish to keep for future breeding and showing. They are sure to have some pullets (young females) which are perfectly healthy and pretty, but have breed faults. A not quite perfect plumage pattern or comb shape will not be a problem in a flock of garden pets.

It is very important to be wary of trying to mix small bantams with large fowl. If they are all running loose around a farmyard it can work, but in a normal set-up of houses and runs they should be kept separately. Many breeders have a pen of commercial hybrids for eggs and a small ornamental breed as their hobby interest. Of course, the tiny breeds will lay more eggs than will be needed for hatching, but not all year round, and they will be tiny eggs.

13

For some people the choice of breed is instant and permanent, perhaps the kind their grandparents kept, or ones that were first created nearby a century ago. Otherwise, visit some poultry shows, preferably large ones, to see as many breeds as possible. Take this book with you so you can get some idea of what to expect of each kind. Make a point of finding some examples of breeds which seem good in the book; they may not appeal as much in the flesh. On the other hand, some breeds which did not catch your attention in the book may have a real charm when you actually see them.

Just as with garden plants, where novice gardeners are often tempted to buy exotic and expensive blooms which they soon lose, it is better to start with a fairly normal 'chicken shaped' breed. By all means feel free to try some with intricate markings. The markings do not affect the hardiness or ease of keeping a bird. It is the structurally unusual breeds, the very tiny, those with heavily feathered feet and so on, which very few beginners are able to cope with. Leave these for a few years on, unless there is an expert nearby for regular guidance.

## Buying bantams

Some poultry shows have a selling section where single birds, pairs and trios (one cock and two hens) are available. You may want a cock and six or more hens, but you are most unlikely to find such a group on offer. The best shows for selling sections are *The Peterborough Autumn Exhibition*, at the East of England Showground, in October, and *The Stafford Poultry Show* at the Stafford Agricultural Showground, in December. At other shows with small or no selling sections it is best to ask at the organiser's desk to be introduced to the owners of breeds in which you are interested. They will not want to sell their best show birds, but will have others at home, so a visit can be arranged.

A few livestock markets still have a small stock section for poultry, pigeons, rabbits, cage-birds, and so on. Melton Mowbray is the best one. Several livestock markets hold special pure breed poultry auctions once or twice a year. They are advertised in farming, smallholding and poultry magazines.

At auctions it is always a case of 'buyer beware', so the ideal is to have an expert friend along to advise on the best and worst lots. Failing that, if you look around the crowd you are fairly sure of seeing some people wearing poultry club badges. Just go and ask someone for guidance. Even if they are not expert themselves, they will probably know: *'That man over there is a show judge, ask him."* Judges always regard getting newcomers on the right track as part of the job. Some of these special sales have judges to 'grade' all the lots before selling starts.

Then, there are advertisements. Most will be found in *Country Smallholding*, *Smallholder* and similar magazines. Also try *Exchange & Mart, Cage & Aviary Birds*, various 'free-ad' type papers and the small ads of local papers in rural areas.

Contact the secretary of *The Poultry Club of Great Britain*, the nearest local poultry club, and the relevant specialist breed club. Between them they should be able to provide some names and telephone numbers. It is for you to decide whether

Visiting agricultural shows enables visitors to see a range of breeds as well as housing. Royal Show. 2000. (David Thear)

to buy the best available locally, or if you are willing to travel a long distance, and possibly pay a lot more for a particular champion strain.

One good option, which includes the long journey, but not the high prices, is to choose a variety which, as far as you can discover, no-one is keeping within, say, a hundred miles. That way, when you have bred some stock for sale, you will have no competition. Many breeds are localised, not because of any real reason beyond the chance factor that it just happens to be where one or two keen breeders live.

## The Organisation of the Poultry Fancy

There is a surprisingly large number of clubs dedicated to the breeding of these old varieties, without which they would soon cease to exist. If you have access to the Internet you can find many sites all over the world dedicated to pure bred poultry, belonging to both private individuals and clubs. It will soon become obvious that there is most activity in those countries with clubs and shows.

Here, we have *The Poultry Club of Great Britain,* run by the elected Poultry Club Council. You do not have to join, but most regular exhibitors do, including all the judges and committee members of the affiliated clubs. The *P.C.G.B.* runs the *National Show,* at Stoneleigh in December, administers judges' exams, publishes newsletters, yearbooks and the *British Poultry Standards* book, sells closed leg rings (their use is optional) and generally does whatever is necessary to hold our hobby together.

Affiliated to the *P.C.G.B.* are about 100 local poultry clubs, the poultry sections of the agricultural shows and the breed clubs. There are about 50 breed clubs, for example, the *Rhode Island Red Club.* There are also organisations such as the *Turkey Club.UK,* the *British Waterfowl Association,* the *Domestic Waterfowl Club* and the *Rare Poultry Society.* The latter covers those breeds with too few breeders to form a separate club, an aspect explained in the next section.

# Breeds

*Bantam breeders comprise a fancy and world of their own.*
(Lewis Wright)

There is a considerable choice when it comes to bantams, including heavy breeds, light breeds, true bantams, hard feather breeds and rare breeds.

## The Heavy Breeds

This is the most popular group of breeds for beginners as they are usually fairly quiet and docile, a definite plus for nervous novice bantam keepers. Expect a range of egg colours from dark brown (Marans) through mid brown shades to creamy tinted. Hens of most of these breeds will go broody and rear their own chicks.

### Australorp

A smart utility type, the Australorp always looks neat and tidy, even if it is not the most colourful breed. The main variety is glossy greenish-black and a few blues are now available. They are good layers of nice tinted eggs.

The main breeding problem for show birds is a tendency for dark skinned faces instead of the bright red required. Black or very dark brown eyes are also required, which is why the dark faces are a persistent problem, as red faces tend to bring light eye colour. As you can imagine, none of this is problematic for breeding as such, it is simply a matter of how perfect (or not) the birds will be. They often win *Best in Show* awards, and as a result there are a lot of expert exhibitors around. They are definitely worth considering by beginners at showing, unless you live near one of the experts, who will beat you every time at the local show. This will not be very encouraging. For those not intending to show, this just means that a lot of Australorp bantams are regularly available for sale - all very nice birds except for minor show faults.

### Barnevelder

Another smart utility breed, this one originated in the Barneveld district of the Netherlands. Large Barnevelders lay very attractive brown eggs, but the bantam eggs are seldom as dark. It would be useful to go to a breeder to buy these so you can see examples of the eggs while you are there.

Whatever shade of egg they lay, Barnevelders are one of the best choices for beginners. They are attractively patterned, easy to breed and keep in good condition with no complications to make management difficult.

Four colour varieties are standardised, but only one is ever seen, the Double Laced. This is a rich combination of reddish-brown and glossy black. Some show halls do not have very good lighting, so you may not appreciate them at a show. Running out on grass in the summer sunlight, a flock of 'Barnies', as they are

Barnevelder bantam male. (Katie Thear)

Miniature Australorp. (Katie Thear)

affectionately known, is stunning. At the shows, competition is not too hot, so here again there is plenty of scope for novices as there is a good chance of winning some breed classes in your first season of showing.

## Brahma

Despite being named after a river in India, large Brahmas were developed in the 1850s from stock imported from the Shanghai area of China. Brahma bantams were developed by W.F. Entwisle of Wakefield, Yorkshire in the 1880s.

They are a sedate and imposing looking breed available in several attractive colours and patterns. Being a feather-footed breed, they need generous sized houses because they should not be let out in mud, although they will certainly appreciate a day on the lawn on nice days. Their bodies are quite plump and rounded and should have fairly short tails and no more than medium length legs, which all adds to the generally compact appearance required. Some faulty Brahma bantams also fail in these respects, giving a too rangy style. They also have small pea combs, which adds to their neatness.

There are five colour varieties of Brahmas: White, Dark, Gold, Light, and Buff Columbian. Darks and Golds are different colour versions of one pattern, and Lights and Buff Columbians are the other pattern. Gold cocks have glossy black breasts, legs and tails. Their necks and backs are shades of gold with black stripes. Gold hens have delicate black markings on a gold ground colour. Buff Columbians of both sexes have black tails, wing markings, foot feathers and neck striping on a buff ground colour. Darks and Lights have the same black markings as Golds and Buff Columbians, but on white ground colour.

Above: Miniature Dark Brahma male. (Katie Thear)

Left: Miniature Croad Langshan hen. (Katie Thear)

## Croad Langshan

These are miniatures of a Chinese breed which was first imported in 1872. They are quite large for bantams and lay good sized tinted eggs. The main colour is black with a green sheen. Whites are also standardised, but very rarely seen. They have slightly feathered shanks and outer toes. This means they do not want to be wading through mud, but are not so heavily feathered on their feet that it is a major problem to keep them looking reasonably presentable. The Croad Langshan Club is a small but enthusiastic group determined to preserve both large and bantam 'Croads' as a genuine old utility pure breed.

## Dorking

Large Dorkings were mentioned by the Romans nearly two thousand years ago. The Dorking bantam cannot claim quite such a history. They were probably first made in the 1880s, but have never attracted many breeders beyond being an interesting sideline for a few keen breeders of large Dorkings. Only one colour variety is ever seen in bantam form, Silver Grey, although four other colours are standardised and seen in the large fowl.

Silver Grey cocks are a striking contrast of a silver-white neck, back, shoulders and flights with the remainder being solid black. Hens have a salmon breast, a white with black striped neck and a grey back and wings. They are low and long bodied, accentuated by a large tail held just above the horizontal. An important characteristic is their extra back toe on each foot, which sticks out and up, not touching the ground.

To keep the colour nice and crisp, a run under some trees would be ideal. In the sun they go an unattractive brassy or yellowish shade. Apart from that they are no trouble to keep and would be a good choice for a back garden conservation centre if the very few existing breeders have any to spare.

Silver Grey Dorking bantam cock. (John Tarren)

## Faverolles

From the village of Faverolles in Northern France, even a single bird of this breed is a Faverolles. They are quite similar to Croad Langshans in being a rather large bantam, also with slightly feathered feet, big enough to lay good sized eggs and the spare cockerels are big enough to roast. As attractive birds to watch running around the garden they have the edge over Croads as they exist in seven colours and also have interesting feathery beards and extra toes like Dorkings.

The most popular variety is the Salmon. The cocks have a black beard, breast, legs and tail, a straw coloured neck and saddle, and the shoulders and back are shades from orange to mahogany. Hens are even better, a delicate cream beard, breast and legs with the neck, back and wings subtle shades of light wheaten-brown.

They are another breed requiring big houses so they can be kept away from mud. During the late summer to autumn moulting season, they may peck at each other's newly growing beard feathers. At this time of year it will hopefully be dry, so they can run out and peck grass instead.

## Frizzle

As the name suggests, these bantams have unusual curled feathers. Every feather curls out from the body, which when shown is given a bath and a blow dry. They are permitted in a wide range of colours and patterns, but patterns do not really work with frizzled feathers, so stick to the self colours, Black, Blue, Buff and White.

Under the frizzling is a perfectly normal, practical hen, capable of laying as well as any other. The only thing is, they cannot really cope with rain, so this is another breed needing large comfortable houses, with the option of time out on the lawn on nice days.

Too many generations of breeding Frizzle to Frizzle will end up producing some rather pathetic looking birds with very sparse and weak feathering. Fortunately they supply their own remedy. Some smooth feathered chicks will be hatched from breeding pens of pure Frizzles, so do not think you have bought some dodgy crossbreds. Smooth feathered cockerels should be killed, as they are of no use, but keep the pullets to breed with your most frizzled cockerels. It is important to use smooth feathered bantams from a strain of Frizzles rather than just any bantam, which would give very unpredictable results.

## Marans

Virtually every poultry keeper knows of Cuckoo Marans and their dark brown eggs. Perhaps fewer know that they are available as bantams as well. Not all of the bantams are as good in egg colour as the large, so it is best to visit the breeder so you can see the eggs being produced for yourself. Like their bigger relations these are easy to keep in a wide range of housing systems. They are quite attractive, but not the most exciting looking breed, which is why not many are seen at the shows, compared with the large numbers kept around the country.

When selecting the best birds to breed from, on the female side it is simplest just to incubate all the darkest brown eggs. With the cockerels you can concentrate more on the birds themselves. Look for sturdy, compact birds with nicely serrated single combs and red ear-lobes. They should be evenly barred all over. Cockerels are naturally lighter in colour overall, but they must not have the big patches of solid white often seen in wing and tail feathers.

A lot of beginners to poultry keeping have large Marans. If you are one of them, why not keep the bantams as well, to become a real Marans specialist?

## New Hampshire Red

These were covered by the Rare Poultry Society until 1997, when their popularity, which had been steadily rising for the previous ten years, reached the level for a separate breed club to be a viable option. The New Hampshire Red Club is still quite small but very active and growing fast. Club members are struggling to keep up with the demand for both large and bantam New Hampshires. This very attractive chestnut-red breed, with contrasting black tails, is everyone's idea of a traditional farmyard chicken and they are especially popular with new poultry keepers.

Obviously an American breed, they were an offshoot from the Rhode Island Reds developed in the neighbouring state. They were not standardised until 1935, so they are not as traditional as they look. They are very popular in the USA and Germany, and being fairly new are also one of the most productive of the pure breeds, in both sizes. As Rhode Islands are now a much darker colour than most novices imagine they should be, many people decide to keep New Hampshires instead when they see live birds of both breeds for the first time.

Some show judges are quite conservative when it comes to giving relatively new breeds *Best in Show* awards, but since 2000 several New Hampshires have man-

Columbian Frizzle bantam male. (Katie Thear)

Cuckoo Marans bantam pullet. (Katie Thear)

aged it, a further encouragement for the club members. At home, both sizes of Reds are good layers of tinted or brown eggs and spare cockerels are quick growing and meaty. There is only the one colour standardised at present, but some Dutch and German breeders have been working on a blue tailed version for some years. New Hampshires would be a very good choice for anyone who likes the idea of becoming a recognised specialist, and having large and bantam versions of the same breed.

## Orpington

Quite large bantams, Orpingtons look even larger than they really are because they have a thick coat of feathers, which gives them a very rounded, matronly appearance. They do not have feathered feet but the body feathers are very close to the ground so they should never be allowed out in muddy conditions. Being very quiet and docile birds they are a good choice for anyone who has never kept poultry before and is a bit nervous with livestock. Orpington hens are good broodies and gentle mothers. Four self colours are standardised, which in order of popularity are Black, Buff, Blue and White.

## Plymouth Rock

This is an American breed, but the body shape of Plymouth Rocks (often just called Rocks) bred in Britain is different; they are taller here than they are there. The original colour variety was Barred. Here again, British breeders have their own style, with narrower barring than is considered necessary in the USA. Buffs are the other popular colour in Rocks, they are a lighter shade than Buff Orpingtons, Buff Wyandottes or Buff Pekins.

Buff bantams of any breed should ideally have a run in the shade, under some trees or on the northern side of a building or wall. Strong sunlight fades the colour, which you may not notice until moulting time when you will see that the new feath-

Buff Plymouth Rock bantam male. The hen is sitting in the box. (Katie Thear)

ers growing through are noticeably darker than the old feathers. Other, rarer colours are Black, Blue, Columbian (like Light Brahmas and Light Sussex), Partridge (like Partridge Wyandottes - see there for full details) and White. Be very aware that a proper Black Plymouth Rock, large or bantam, is pure glossy greenish-black with bright yellow shanks and feet. Do not confuse them with the commercial hybrids called Black Rocks which have a lot of brown feathers mixed in.

They are a normal shaped breed and are easy to keep in a wide range of housing systems. Barreds and Buffs are obviously easier to buy as there are many more breeders. Those intending to start showing will choose them if they like a competitive challenge, or they might decide to track down one of the other colours for something rarer.

## Rhode Island Red

Another American breed, this is probably one of the best known poultry breeds to people who don't know anything about chickens. Most people are surprised to find that they are a much darker colour than they were expecting, a very deep and glossy chocolate-red.

They are very easy to keep, the only problem is that the deep colour seems to have brought with it a tendency to poor feather quality; the cocks often have tatty tails for no apparent reason. Where show birds are concerned, after they have had a pre-show bath (see *Showing* section), apply some hair conditioner (I am not joking). Rhodes are best kept on good outside grassed runs.

A breeding trio of prize-winning Rhode Island Red bantams. (Katie Thear)

## Sussex

As with the Rhodes, nearly everyone has heard of Light Sussex. Very few know of the other six colours. As the name suggests, it is very much a British breed. Large Sussex were one of the main breeds traditionally kept on farms, and in their smaller way, Sussex bantams are just as useful, laying well, hatching their own chicks and the cockerels are big enough to eat.

At the shows there are many expert exhibitors of Light Sussex bantams. Staging a snow white bodied bird with perfect black neck, wing and tail markings is not easy. Nor are the self White Sussex, which also have to be absolutely pure, snow-white. New exhibitors will do better if they choose one or more of the other varieties. If you just want them to run about in your garden then none of this matters, the fact that there are a lot of perfectionist breeders out there just means there are lots of Light, and a few White Sussex available every autumn.

Buff Sussex have the same black markings as Light Sussex, but on a buff body instead of white. Fewer are shown, so they do not need to be quite as perfect as the Lights. Speckled Sussex are mainly an attractive mahogany colour, with white feather tips and a black band between the white and the mahogany. They are easier to breed than this sounds. The most common fault is having the plumage in general being a touch too tight to the body compared with the other varieties of Sussex, which are fuller feathered.

Silver Sussex have similar neck markings to Lights, but instead of white bodies, Silvers have black bodies with white edges to most of the feathers. Red Sussex are the colour people expect Rhode Islands to be, with the same black markings as Lights. Brown Sussex cocks have black breasts, legs and tails, the remainder being

rich mahogany with black centre striping. The hens have brown necks with black centre stripes, brown backs and wings, with very fine black peppering and a pale wheaten brown breast.

Reds and Browns are both rarer than many Rare Breeds. A new variety, the Coronation Sussex - like the Light, but with blue markings instead of black - has been created, but at the time of writing (2002) have not been standardised.

Silver Sussex bantam hen. (Katie Thear)

## Wyandotte

lndirectly named after a tribe of Native Americans, the Wyandotte's more direct connection arose from the fact that this was also the name of a ship owned by the family of one of the early breeders, Mr. Fred Houdlette.

Wyandotte bantams, and to a lesser extent the large version, are one of the most popular pure poultry breeds all over the world. At some of the huge shows regularly held in Germany, well over a thousand Wyandottes can be seen. Why are they so popular?

Firstly, they are very easy to keep healthy, smart and looking good. They have neat rose combs following the line of their heads, tidy rounded bodies with short tails giving an overall compact bird with an attractive combination of curves. With no big combs, long tails or feathered feet to worry about, there is simply nothing to get broken.

Ease of management enables breeders to concentrate on the other great attraction of Wyandottes, a huge range of colours and patterns to choose from.

Those with the time and expertise often choose White Wyandottes. These are fairly easy to breed, the problem is keeping them snow-white. As an extra complication White Wyandottes are required to have bright yellow feet. The 'Catch-22' here is that to get the yellow feet you feed maize and/or let them run out to eat grass. If you do that there is a great danger of getting creamy plumage instead of the snow-white required. A way round this is to keep them inside or in shady runs.

Black Wyandottes are another variety which are more difficult than they look. A similar problem, sound glossy black plumage, with no odd white feathers or white in the fluff near the skin is very difficult to obtain with the bright yellow feet also required on Blacks. Many Black Wyandottes, especially hens, have dark shaded feet.

Blues and Buffs are the other two self colours. Both are quite rare and although producing perfect specimens is not easy either, there is more chance here for beginners to become well known as a 'leading breeder' fairly quickly.

There are four colour combinations of the Laced pattern:

Silver Laced Wyandotte bantam hen. (Katie Thear)

Silver Laced - white feathers with black lacing

Gold Laced - rich golden bay with black lacing

Blue Laced - red-brown with bluish grey-lacing

Buff Laced - rich buff (sometimes, but not ideal, brick-red) with white lacing

Silver Laced have to be bred separately, but the other three can be bred together as one combined flock. This makes them an excellent choice for those who like to see a colourful mixed group of bantams and have not yet organised a range of separate houses for proper pedigree breeding. Expect these results:

Gold Laced x Gold Laced - 100% Gold Laced
Gold Laced x Blue Laced - 50% Gold Laced, 50% Blue Laced
Gold Laced x Buff Laced - 100% Blue Laced
Blue Laced x Blue Laced - 50% Blue Laced, 25% Gold Laced, 25% Buff Laced
Blue Laced x Buff Laced - 50% Blue Laced, 50% Buff laced
Buff Laced x Buff Laced - 100% Buff Laced

In all cases it does not matter which way round you have the crossing, ie, which is the cock or which is the hen. Only a small proportion of Laced Wyandotte chicks grow up to have really good markings, but the not quite so good ones are still very pretty and are easily sold to the majority who are not obsessive perfectionists such as we show people.

Barred Wyandottes are sharply striped, black and white, across the feathers. The barring is not quite as narrow as that of Barred Plymouth Rocks, but is more defined than any of the other barred or cuckoo (fuzzy barring, like Marans) breeds.

Columbian Wyandottes are the same pattern as Light Sussex, but the black neck stripes are narrower, giving a lighter overall appearance. Large Columbian Wyandottes were first shown at the Columbian Exhibition at Chicago in 1893, hence the name.

Red Wyandottes are the same colour as Red Sussex, rich mahogany with Columbian black markings. There are probably less than five breeders of Red Wyandottes in Britain at present, so clearly supply is very limited.

Partridge Wyandottes are really two separate varieties under one name, as exhibition cocks and hens cannot both be bred from one strain. 'Cock breeders' and 'Pullet breeders' have been completely separated into two varieties in Germany, a logical step which we should follow. Show cocks have solid glossy black breasts contrasting with the neck and saddle hackles which are bright golden yellow shades with sharp black centre striping. Pullet breeding cocks have a lot of brown mixed in their breasts and the hackles are a shade darker.

Show hens (bred from pullet breeder cocks) have a yellowish ground colour with three very fine black rings on every feather. Cock-breeder hens have sharp neck markings, but their bodies are darker than the show hens and are fuzzy and irregularly marked. They are never shown, but just kept at home as breeders.

Silver Pencilleds are the same patterns, with white replacing the gold shades. Most people keep pullet-breeders, which is a shame because the show cocks seen in Holland and Germany are striking birds. Other colours occasionally seen are: Salmon (as Faverolles), Speckled (as Sussex) and Black Mottled (black with white spots).

# The Light Breeds

With the three exceptions of Araucanas, Silkies and Welsummers, the Light Breeds lay white or creamy shelled eggs, seldom, if ever, go broody to hatch them and are more active birds and better fliers than the Heavy Breeds. Run fences need to be at least 1.8m (6ft) high to keep them in. Light breeds will live on and lay well for many years, but most are only shown in their first year of age, after which they get too big and fat, thus losing the slim and elegant style required. Also, most Light Breeds have white ear lobes which seldom stay pure snow white and perfectly formed for many months after reaching maturity.

## Ancona

Only one colour has ever been accepted in Anconas, black with neat white feather tips. New breeders are often very surprised when their first batch of chicks first feather up looking like penguins, with white breasts and black backs. Don't panic, this is just a juvenile phase! As they moult into their first adult plumage they change to the expected pattern. Anconas can most definitely only be shown for one year as in each subsequent year the white spots get bigger, losing the neatness of their first year. Shanks and feet are yellow with some black spots, which are kept a nice bright colour by allowing them out to eat grass and including some kibbled maize in their diet. Most Anconas have medium sized single combs, upright on cocks, over to one side on hens. A few breeders have the rarer rose combed sub-variety.

They do not go broody, so an incubator is needed. Anconas can be nervous and wild, which can be reduced by handling the chicks as often as possible from three weeks old to maturity. This advice applies to all of the light breeds.

Miniature Ancona bantam male. (Katie Thear)

## Araucana

The members of the Araucana Club can hardly keep up with the demand for this breed. It is their unusual blue and green shelled eggs which attract all the interest. They originally came from South America, mainly Chile. There are two types, tailed and rumpless. Both are in large and bantam versions, all in several colours.

Rumpless Araucanas are rarer and not to everyone's taste, but they are the 'original and genuine'. Not only do they not have a tail, they do not even have a parson's nose! They have another very unusual feature, tufts of feathers sticking out of their ears, sometimes called ear-rings. This is caused by a semi-lethal gene, so many birds do not have them. To the non-exhibitor a nice flock of these birds, even without ear-tufts, will be a very interesting collection.

The most popular colour variety of tailed Araucana bantams is the Lavender, near enough to be able to say you are getting blue eggs from blue hens. These have feathered head crests and beards, which add to their charm.

Parents of children who are reluctant to eat eggs may find these natural Easter eggs are more appealing. Araucanas seem to be attracting a lot of interest on the Internet, some of which is a bit odd, but worth a look.

## Hamburgh

Four very pretty patterned varieties of Hamburghs exist: Gold Spangled, Silver Spangled, Gold Pencilled and Silver Pencilled. The exact details would need more space than this book can give, so in brief:

Black Araucana bantam. (Katie Thear)

Rumpless Araucana. (John Tarren)

Silver Spangled are white with a large round black spot on each feather end. Some hens appear mostly black because the spots tend to overlap. The large tail feathers of both cocks and hens are particularly striking.

Gold Spangled are rich mahogany with the same black spots. Solid black tails are normal in Golds because mahogany tails with black spots were unobtainable. At least one breeder has now done it. Gold Spangled is a very rare colour.

As may be guessed, Gold and Silver Pencilleds are the same pattern in two colours. Pencilled Hamburghs need to be 'double mated' (see Poultry Terms section) as males and females are very differently marked. Gold Pencilled females are most often seen. They have a bright gold ground colour, with fine black barring, except for the head and neck which are clear gold. Silver Pencilleds have a white ground colour. The pullet breeder cocks needed to produce them are the same pattern and are often 'hen feathered' (see Poultry Terms section).

Despite their name, exhibition Pencilled cocks have hardly any pencilling. Their bodies are clear gold or silver with a black tail. The tail feathers should have a fine gold or silver edging. Cock breeder hens have clear (gold or silver) necks, breasts and shoulders with irregular black markings on the back and tail.

All varieties have rose combs, dark eyes, white ear lobes and bluish-grey shanks and feet. Plumage is moderately close and tight to the body, and the tails are very large. For many years Hamburgh bantams have been quite big, not much smaller than large Hamburghs. Breeders in Germany and the Netherlands have been much better at keeping their breeds correctly to the weights specified in the breed standards. Recently some European strains of Silver Spangled Hamburgh bantams have arrived here, causing some controversy within the Hamburgh Club and poultry show judges generally.

Black and Blue Leghorn bantams. (Katie Thear)

Gold Pencilled Hamburghs. (Katie Thear)

# Leghorn

The many millions of white egg laying hybrids in the world have been developed from strains of smallish, large Leghorns. Large exhibition Leghorns are rather bigger than the utility type. To further complicate matters, there are several different exhibition types around the world. There is not space here to give full details, but to give two extreme examples; British Leghorns have relatively large combs and small tails and American Leghorns have smaller combs and really huge tails.

Rose combed Leghorns are standardised but very rare. Most have large single combs which should be upright on cocks, and flop over to one side on hens. Most cockerels only have upright combs for a few months after maturity, after which they flop over like their sisters' combs. Because of this, far more females are seen at shows than males. At home they are good layers of white eggs.

Twelve colours are standardised and extra new ones are also sometimes seen. The White and Black varieties are most popular, and often win show championships. Leghorns have yellow feet, which means these two varieties have the same problems as the same colours in Wyandottes. Brown Leghorns are a lot more colourful than their name suggests. Cocks have glossy black breasts, underparts and tails with shades of orange to red necks and backs. The hens have salmon breasts, yellow (with black stripes) necks and brown wings and backs. Buff and Blue Leghorns are both very attractive and deserve to be more popular than they are. Exchequer Leghorns are an unusual variety, a random mix of black and white.

29

## Minorca

Minorca bantam. (John Tarren)

Blue and White Minorcas are both standardised, but rarely seen. I do not remember ever seeing a White. Black is the main variety, and one of the reasons for Minorcas not being as popular as they used to be. Black breeds still frequently win major show awards, but are not a popular choice with those wanting pretty bantams for the garden.

Minorcas have large single combs, large wattles and very large white ear lobes. The lobes often suffer from spots and scabs. When older, the white spreads to the eye-lids and face, which should all be cherry red. As with Leghorns, cocks' combs also flop over a few months after maturity, giving them a short show life.

Having said all that, a Minorca in perfect show condition is a very beautiful bird. The show judges are well aware how difficult they are to produce and so good ones often win those coveted *Best in Show* awards. The Minorca Club has about one hundred enthusiastic members, most of whom probably started with other breeds and switched to Minorcas after they gained experience with easier kinds. I advise you to do the same. Any beginners who see them, and instantly want them, should buy direct from an established expert, and keep in touch. Club members will be happy to give long term advice.

## Poland

Polands have a big ball of feathers on their heads with a very tiny, sometimes completely absent, horned comb in front. The name is derived from 'polled' rather than the country. The single breed, as defined in Britain and the USA, is divided into two in Germany, the Netherlands and several other countries. One group is the White Crested, which obviously have white crests, but the remainder of the plumage is another colour, black, blue or cuckoo barred. They have normal wattles, unlike the other group which are bearded. This other group, which in Europe are called Paduaners, have six varieties: Gold Laced, Silver Laced, Chamois (Buff Laced), Black, Blue and White.

They attract brisk bidding at the specialist poultry auctions as they are exotic looking birds to strut around a country garden. I suspect most of these birds soon look a sorry sight, as a free range life in the garden or farmyard of a beginner is exactly the wrong place for Polands.

To keep the crests in good order they should be kept in when it is raining. Special drinkers are best to avoid wet crests. For single birds or pairs in cage type accommodation, use large size budgerigar type drinkers. Polands can dip their beaks in daintily, without getting soggy crests or beards. For larger groups some breeders use large, heavy pottery dog bowls with wire netting over the top to hold the crests out of the water. These must be kept topped up at all times.

Polands are a breed needing special care, and novices should follow the advice that experts are happy to give. For something even more exotic, Frizzled Feathered Polands are also available in all colours.

White Crested Black Poland bantam male. (Katie Thear)

## Redcap

These are more often called by their full name 'Derbyshire Redcaps'. There is a Derbyshire Redcap Club so they are not in the Rare Breeds section despite being very rare, especially the bantams. The club only has about 40 members, and most of them only keep the large fowl. Also, Redcaps are unknown outside Britain, so the very small group here with the bantams have the total world population between them. Redcaps are related to Gold Spangled Hamburghs, and are very similar except for having larger combs and red ear lobes. Redcap cocks have black breasts instead of the spangled breasts of Hamburghs. Those willing to breed Redcap bantams for many years will be making a valuable contribution to conservation.

## Scots Dumpy

As can be guessed from the name, this is a native Scottish breed with very short legs. Most are Cuckoo barred, with a few Blacks also around. They are quite good layers and excellent broodies and mothers, thus making them a good second breed for those whose other interest is a non-sitting type.

Short legged exhibition quality cocks are often not very fertile because they have trouble mating. Some longer legged birds are always bred each year, so for best results use a longer legged cock with your best short legged hens. Also the 'creeper' gene which gives the very short legs is a semi-lethal gene, so a breeding trio of all short legged birds will produce 25% dead embryos anyway. The long-leg x short-leg mating does not give any dead embryos for this reason. Long-leg in this context does not mean very tall, just a bit taller than the ideal Dumpy.

31

## Scots Grey

This is the other Scottish breed. There is only one colour variety, the Barred. The barring should be black and white, sharply defined especially on the large wing feathers. Some of the best birds have a few odd black feathers. These are just pulled out for shows. A more serious problem, usually seen on cocks, is partly white feathers. This mostly occurs on tail feathers, where the ends of the feathers are properly barred, but the bottom half near the skin is white. (See page 9). Most breeders will have more cockerels than they can keep each year, so any poor examples can be eaten.

White Silkie hen. (Katie Thear)

Greys are good layers and very charming little birds, quite elegant and stream-lined in style. They have medium sized combs, wattles and tails; also there are no feathered legs or any other difficulties in keeping them healthy and happy. This is an excellent choice for the garden or farmyard, for the beginner or more experi-enced bantam keeper.

## Silkie

Marco Polo, the famous medieval explorer, thought Silkies to be a cross between a chicken and a rabbit when he first saw them in China. Since then they have become a common sight in the countryside as they are very good broodies. Pure Silkie hens can lose chicks by hanging, however! They get caught up in the hair-like feathers, so Silkie crosses are more popular as sitters than pure bred birds. Silkies used to be a halfway bird between large fowl and bantams, but there are now separate large and bantam versions. The bantams are very tiny, cocks weigh just 600gm (22oz) and hens 500gm (18oz).

When selecting the best birds for breeding make sure there is no reversion to normal feathering. Tail and wing feathers are the first to show signs of losing silki-ness. All the skin, and even the meat, if ever you eat one, is dark blue. This is another breed characteristic which can be lost if the wrong birds are bred from.

In the Far East, black chicken soup is considered a delicacy, a fact which might encourage a reluctant family to eat the spare cockerels.

Silkies have yet more unusual features: an extra hind toe on each foot, feathered feet, a fluffy head crest and in front of the crest a 'cushion comb', a small fleshy lump with a groove running across. Beards are an optional extra. White Silkies are the best quality, and the most frequently seen. A few Black bantams are available, but Blues, Golds and Partridge, as seen on large Silkies are not yet available as bantams.

Silkies can be kept well under any housing system, but special care is needed for show birds, and they should not be allowed out in wet weather. Bathing and blow-

Scots Dumpy bantam male and female. (John Tarren)

drying are necessary. A lot of Silkies, of a sort, are widely available and quite cheap. Good quality show stock will cost more and should be bought from someone with a good track record of show success.

## Welsummer

Named after the Dutch village, Welsum, these are the ultimate traditional farmyard breed. Very dark brown eggs coming from prettily patterned birds makes this one of our most popular breeds, far more so than the numbers seen around the shows would suggest. Many beginners choose them, and they are wise to do so. They are best kept in houses with large grassy runs as they are active birds which need exercise. The hens sometimes go broody, but not often, so an incubator or another type of bantam will be needed for hatching. Egg shell colour does vary a bit, so to keep this most important characteristic, select the darkest brown eggs for hatching.

Welsummer cocks are a modified Black-Red pattern. Other Black-Red birds (Black Red Old English Game, Brown Leghorns, Partridge Wyandottes) have solid black breasts. Welsummers have brown and black mixed colour breasts, rather like pullet breeder Partridge Wyandottes. The neck and saddle hackles do not have the black striping seen in these other breeds. Welsummer hens are again of the same basic pattern as Brown Leghorn, but of a darker and more reddish overall shade. Welsummer hens have light coloured feather shafts which stand out from the general reddish-brown shade.

The best show birds may, or may not, be the ones laying the best dark brown eggs. Because the eggs are the main point of interest in Welsummers, perfect show birds may not be bred very often. There is also a Silver variety, but not many people keep them. (See Welbars in the Rare Breeds section. Welbars are another colour and are Welsummer in all but name).

33

# True Bantam Breeds

Dutch bantam male. (John Tarren)

Porcelaine Booted bantam. Booteds are also classified as a rare breed . (Katie Thear)

Barbu d'Uccle Millefleur. (Katie Thear)

Quail Barbu de Watermael. (Katie Thear)

Lavender Pekin male. Note some 'brassiness' in the plumage. (Katie Thear)

Black Rosecomb male. (Katie Thear)

34

Black-Tailed White Japanese male. (Katie Thear)

Breeding trio of Gold Sebrights. (Katie Thear)

Gold Partridge Dutch bantam hen. (Katie Thear)

Nankins, also classified a rare breed. (Katie Thear)

Lavender Quail Barbu d'Anvers. (Katie Thear)

Silver Sebright hen showing the lacing on its plumage. (Katie Thear)

# The Hard Feather Breeds

These are mostly kept by enthusiastic, experienced exhibitors rather than beginners. Old English Game bantams are by far the most popular breed of all at British poultry shows. For competitive minded breeders, with the patience and determination to catch up with and then overtake the skill of the established breeders, they are a real challenge. At poultry auctions OEG bantams do not seem to be attracting much interest nowadays. Perhaps beginners are choosing an easier path to the top.

The fine details of body shape and 'handling' is more important than colour and markings on most of this group. This is difficult to describe properly in a small book like this and, anyway, these specialist breeds can only be appreciated by direct contact with experts to explain the finer points.

## Old English Game

At home, OEG bantams are the best layers and broodies of the Hard Feather breeds. Hens not good enough to show are widely available for quite low prices. Such hens could be a good buy for hatching and rearing one of the non-sitting breeds.

Although these bantams were never directly used for cock-fighting they have enough aggression from their large fowl ancestors to need appropriate housing arrangements to keep the cocks apart. On the positive side, this boldness means that they are very tame with people. As pets they really shine. If you want bantams to eat from your hand or be picked up and stroked by your children, then take a close look at this breed. Their aggressive tendencies are directed solely at other chickens.

They are very popular at the shows, and are bred in a huge range of colours. They should have broad, muscular breasts tapering to the tail end, giving a cone shape when handled. Their tails are quite small. As many people point out, OEG bantams are nothing like a miniature of the original large fowl Game Cocks. There was a controversial change in the style in the 1920s.

Apart from the wide range of standardised colours, 'off colour' OEG bantams (any colour or pattern that crops up) can be shown, unlike other breeds where only perfectly coloured or marked specimens are considered worth having. This is true in OEG because there is so much emphasis on body shape and muscle tone. Free range is essential to keep them fit.

## Indian Game

Despite the name the original large fowl version was created in Cornwall. They are called Cornish in the USA. From the 1920s on they were developed into a very broad bodied meat breed and were used to produce modern broiler chickens.

Indian Game bantams have the same massive bodies on short thick legs as the full sized version, but on a smaller scale. With this physique the best show cocks are often not very fertile as they just cannot manage it. Most breeders keep longer legged cocks as breeders which are mated with short legged hens.

They are not everyone's favourites, but they do have a charm of their own. Three colour varieties are standardised: Darks, Jubilees and Blues. Dark cocks are black. Dark hens are 'double laced', black and mahogany brown. Jubilee cocks are mostly white with reddish brown markings. Jubilee hens are 'double laced', white and red. Blue cocks are blue and Blue hens are 'double laced' blue and mahogany brown.

## Modern Game

The opposite of Indians, these are very small bodied birds with long thin legs. There are 13 colours. Large Modern Game were developed in the 1880s as a show breed by the generation of judges and breeders who were too young to have had any contact with Game Cocks before 1849. They imagined, wrongly, that a bird with more 'reach' would have had an advantage in a fight.

Only a few historically minded enthusiasts keep large Moderns in existence, but Modern Game bantams are bred by hundreds of keen exhibitors around the world. These elegant, tiny bantams are very tame and are too small to scratch up your flower beds and so are excellent pets for the suburban bantam keeper.

# Asian Hard Feather Breeds

Until recently these were in the Rare Breeds section, but the whole group has gone out together to a specialist club. Most are still too rare to be available outside the ranks of established breeders. Two are worth consideration by the beginner with a taste for the unusual. One look at a Malay or a Ko-Shamo will dispel any doubts about birds being direct descendants of the dinosaurs!

## Malay

Like Indian Game these are traditionally associated with Cornwall, but along different lines. Malays are a very tall breed, with very long legs and neck which is accentuated by their having very scanty plumage. They have a compact walnut comb and very small (or no) wattles and thick beaks. Their eyebrow bones are prominent and the eye irises are a light yellow colour. All this combines to give the desired *'cruel and morose expression'*. The main colour varieties are Black-Red cocks with Wheaten or Cinnamon hens, White, Black, Spangled and Pile (Orange and white). Size, shape and character is more important than colour.

## Ko-Shamo

Although a very ancient breed in Japan, none were known in Britain before 1980. They are rapidly attracting many new breeders. As evidence of this, 86 were entered at the 2001 National Show, a lot more than other more established breeds. In Japan, they are very popular and are even kept in small houses on the balconies of apartment blocks. As may be imagined, if they are kept in these circumstances the cocks do not crow very much and it is not much of a noise when they do. One breeder I know here had seven Ko-Shamo cocks, and his neighbour did not even know he had any cocks.

# Soft-Feather Heavy Breed Bantams

Rhode Island Red bantam male. (Katie Thear)

Barred Plymouth Rock bantam female. (Katie Thear)

Light Sussex bantams. (Katie Thear)

Miniature New Hampshire Red male. (John Tarren)

Salmon Faverolles bantam hen. (Katie Thear)

Black Orpington bantams. (Katie Thear)

Partridge Wyandotte bantam hen. (John Tarren)

White German Langshan bantams, classified as a rare breed. (Katie Thear)

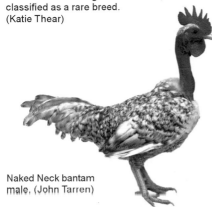

Naked Neck bantam male. (John Tarren)

Barnevelder bantam hen. (John Tarren)

Spangled Orloff bantam, classified as a rare breed. (Katie Thear)

Frizzle bantam hen. (Katie Thear)

Ko-Shamo male demonstrating his upright stance. The female is in the background. (Katie Thear)

Yamato-Gunkei, a rare Asian and hard feather bantam male and female. (Katie Thear)

As the standard says, they have an *"Upright stance. Alert, confident bearing. Full of character and attitude."* Three different comb types are allowed, all variations on a theme of small, compact fleshy lumps. Ko-Shamo do not have wattles, instead having dewlapped throats. The skin on their head and throat is smooth on young birds, but becomes thick and wrinkled after they are about two years old. This is all part of their character. They do not really 'look the part' until they are three years old. The beak should be short, thick and rather hawk like.

Plumage is very sparse and scanty, showing bare patches in places. The tail is very short and curved down. It is called a 'prawn tail' in Japan. Most bantams have two lines of scales down the front of their shanks (the scaled part of the leg), but Ko-Shamo should have thick legs with four or five lines of small scales. Several colour varieties are seen, but body shape, head character and other similar details of type are more important.

Both Ko-Shamo and Malays are regarded as downright ugly by many people, but they have a real charm of their own. Children and teenagers who need convincing about the 'street cred' of bantam keeping should warm to breeds whose official breed standard insists on *'attitude'* or a *'cruel and morose expression'*.

# The True Bantams

These are very much ornamental breeds, so do not expect masses of eggs from True Bantams. Most of them need special care and attention, which only the most organised beginners will be able to provide.

## Barbu d'Anvers

We use the French name for 'bearded' for this Belgian breed. The Flemish name, Antwerpse Baard Krielen, sounds good, too. They are quite small, adult cocks weighing 800gm (28oz) down to 570gm (20oz) for pullets, but are big enough to lead a normal free range life. Barbu d'Anvers do not have feathered feet or other difficult features, which makes them the best of the True Bantams for beginners

These little birds have a proud, strutting bearing, full of personality. They have neat rose combs which should be broad and low. Some strains have higher growing combs, which is not ideal. Under their beaks they have feathery beards.

Many colour varieties are available, including the Quail pattern in several colour variants: Normal Quail, Blue Quail, Lavender Quail and Silver Quail.

Normal Quails have creamy-ochre breast contrasting with their neck, back, wings and tail, which are dark umber-brown with ochre markings. Normal Quails can be crossed with any of the other three Quail variants, but it is best not to cross the variants with each other. (eg, not Blue Quail x Lavender Quail).

Black Barbu d'Anvers may not be the colourful first choice for garden runabouts, but they are usually best shaped and so often win *Best of Breed* at the shows. Blues and Cuckoos can both be crossed with Blacks, but should not be crossed with each other.

Because there is some scope for crossing colours within the breed, it is worth considering becoming a Barbu d'Anvers specialist.

## Barbu du Grubbe

These are a rumpless version of Barbu d'Anvers. They are even rare in Belgium!

## Barbu d'Uccle

Ukkelse Baard Krielen in Flemish, these are also from Belgium and also have beards, but there the similarity ends. They are bigger than d'Anvers, have single combs and, most noticeably, heavily feathered feet. These footings are quite brittle and easily broken, which makes them a difficult breed to keep looking good.

Many colours are permitted, but only three are seen regularly: Millefleur, Porcelaine and Black Mottled. The last is obviously black with white spots.

Millefleur is the same as Speckled Sussex, but a shade lighter orange-red instead of the mahogany of the Sussex. The black and white spots are the same.

Porcelaine is the same pattern, but diluted by the Lavender gene. Black becomes lavender and orange-red is changed to shades of creamy-pinkish-ochre.

Because Millefleur and Porcelaine are only associated with this breed many people get confused, thinking these are the breed names rather than the colour names.

# Soft Feather Light Breed Bantams

Welbar bantam hen. (John Tarren)

Welsummer bantam hen. (John Tarren)

Lavender Araucana bantam. (Katie Thear)

Ancona bantams. (Katie Thear)

Silver Spangled Hamburgh bantam hen. (Katie Thear)

Blue Leghorn bantam hen. (Katie Thear)

Miniature White Leghorns. (Katie Thear)

Champion Andalusian bantam cock. This Light breed is also classified as a rare breed. (Katie Thear)

Chamois Poland bantam. (John Tarren)

Black-Red Yokohama cock, classified as a rare breed. (John Tarren)

Vorwerk breeding pair, also classified as a rare breed. (Katie Thear)

Rare breed Red Saddled Yokohama. (John Tarren)

43

## Barbu d'Everberg

This is a Rumpless d'Uccles that is seldom seen.

## Barbu de Watermael

The smallest of the Belgian bantams, pullets will come into lay when only weighing 450gm (15½oz). These perky little birds are also suitable for beginners. They are generally very similar to Barbu d'Anvers, but are smaller and have a modest feathered head crest behind a rose comb. Watermael crests are similar to Araucana crests, much smaller than Poland crests. They are bred in the same colours as d'Anvers.

## Dutch

These are even smaller than Watermaels. The maximum weight allowed for an adult cock is 550gm (20oz), with pullets maturing at just 400gm (14oz). Unlike many other bantam breeds, these weight limits are obeyed, making Dutch the smallest breed in the world. In shape they are simply classic chickens in miniature. They do have large fanned tails so do not think that these tiny birds can be kept in tiny houses, for tails will be broken, which needlessly spoils the look of them. Even so, someone with just the end part of a garden for their bantam area will be able to keep several colours of Dutch. By this, I mean enough birds of each variety to keep the strains going at a good quality for many generations, not just an odd one or two of each.

Dutch bantams were not standardised in the Netherlands until 1906, but had been bred for many years before. Some were shown in Britain in 1922, but they soon died out. They were not seen here again until the late 1960s, and were a Rare Breed until 1982 when the Dutch Bantam Club was formed. Now there are numbers of entries at shows all over the country, and many more are kept as garden pets by non-exhibitors.

Combs are of the normal, single type, upright on both sexes, and ideally with five nice, even wedge shaped points. Ear lobes are white and as near circular as possible. Because the lobes are quite small they are not as difficult to keep in condition as other white lobed breeds. The general body type is very normal, with large fanned tails which should be held at an angle to give a smooth, curved sweeping top line when viewed in profile. The tail should not be so high that there is a sharp angle between the back and the tail.

The two most popular colours are Gold Partridge and Silver Partridge. Other varieties include: Yellow Partridge, Blue-gold Partridge, Blue-silver Partridge, Cuckoo Partridge, Pile, Cuckoo, Black, Blue, Lavender, and White. The Dutch Club uses English translations of Dutch terminology for the colours. For example, Cuckoo Partridge, which has the advantage of being more understandable for beginners, is called Crele by British fanciers generally. Some of the varieties can be bred together, for example Gold Partridge and Blue-gold Partridge. This does not mean you can cross the colours anyhow. If you join your local poultry club you will soon get to know the nearest person with a fair knowledge of poultry genetics if you need help.

Porcelaine Barbu d'Uccle male and female in their cage at a poultry show. (Katie Thear)

Blue Quail Barbu de Watermael hen. (Katie Thear)

# Japanese (Chabo in Japan and many other countries)

With their very short legs, they look as if they are sitting down even when standing up, and some people might think they are the product of a mad genetic engineer. In fact, Chabo were depicted in Japanese paintings back in 1603. Japan closed itself off from the rest of the world between 1636 and 1867, so not many were spread around the world until after then. The Dutch had limited trading arrangements between 1636 and 1867 via a small Japanese island, hence a Chabo cock was available for Jan Steen to include in his painting *The Poultry Yard* (circa 1660).

The other unmistakable feature is the long tail held upright, reaching much higher than their heads. Avoid buying birds with tails over to one side, a common fault. (Watch birds closely for some time to be sure). The fault is called wry tail, when the tails are bent over nearly all the time.

Japanese have normal, upright single combs, medium to large size. Over the centuries several sub-varieties have been developed: Silkie feathered, Frizzle feathered and Bearded.

Many colours exist, but the two most associated with Japanese are Black-Tailed-White and Black-Tailed-Buff. Neither of these varieties should have any black markings in their necks, but they often do. However these birds can be useful for breeding, as continual breeding from birds with correct clear necks results in a loss of black in tail.

Housing Japanese must be designed to suit their unique physique. They cannot manage perches and will happily sleep on the floor, which as a result must be covered with wood shavings and regularly cleaned. Cleanliness is vital as their breast and wing feathers are touching the ground. They are mostly kept in, but will certainly enjoy, and benefit from a nice day out on the lawn. Think along similar lines (but in larger sizes) to the many people whose pet rabbits mostly live in hutches and have movable runs for their outings.

45

# Hard-Feather Bantam Breeds

National Champion Ko-Shamo. (Katie Thear)

Silver Duckwing Modern Game bantam hen. (John Tarren)

Left: Rumpless Game bantam. (John Tarren)

Right: Malay bantam. (John Tarren)

Furness Old English Game bantam hen. (Katie Thear)

46

Jubilee Indian Game bantam. (John Tarren)

A bantam collection in a well-ventilated house with perching and scratching facilities. The birds include: Watermael, Citron Sabelpoot, Blue Pile Dutch, Tuzo, Yamato and Blue Pekin. (Katie Thear)

Yokohamas need plenty of room for their tails when perching. (Katie Thear)

Will Burdett judging at the National Poultry Show. (John Tarren)

A group of Lavender Pekins enjoying the lawn. (David Thear)

The Japanese Bantam Club has about 70 keen members who enter over 200 birds between them at the annual club show at Newbury. This sums up 'Japs' nicely: not to everyone's taste, but enthusiastically bred by those who like them.

## Pekin

These little balls of feathers are one of the most popular breeds of all. They are quiet and tame birds, making them good pets. Having heavily feathered feet and profuse body plumage which also touches the ground means that the comments on housing and management stated for Japanese (above) also apply to Pekins. I have seen enough mud-caked Pekins over the years to know that many people do not appreciate this.

The first Pekins seen in Britain were part of the booty from the looting of the Emperor's Palace at Beijing (Peking) by a combined British and French force in 1860, during the Opium Wars. Under these circumstances it is not surprising that not much is known of their earlier history. Since then a wide range of colour varieties has been developed. The first birds were Buffs. Pekins today are more profusely feathered and have shorter legs than the originals. The best show birds 'pose' with their fronts down and tails up. This is called the 'Pekin Tilt'.

Buffs should be a nice bright, even shade. Feathers should be buff to the skin; many faulty birds are white at the fluff near the skin. Other faults are white or black in wings and/or tail.

Blacks and Black-mottled (black with white spots) are both very good, and often win at the shows. The same can be true of Blues and Lavenders, but good coloured birds are more difficult to breed.

Whites are excellent, and easy to breed, but they are a lot more difficult to keep pure white. Many White Pekins seen at shows look rather pale in the face, as though they could do with some time out on the lawn, but didn't get it for fear of getting dirty.

Partridge Pekin female. (Katie Thear)

Black Pekins.
Many breeders prefer to keep Pekins and other feathered legged breeds indoors so that the legs do not become caked with mud. (Katie Thear)

Partridge Pekins should be the same very precise pattern as Partridge Wyandottes but are never as good. Breeders are gradually improving the markings, but there is still some way to go.

As there are many breeders, Pekins are almost certain to be available at all poultry auctions and show selling sections. The hens go broody and are good mothers but it is best to trim their foot feathers as they can drag eggs out of the nest by mistake. Fertility may be a problem, but is easily improved by trimming some of the feathers around the bottoms of both sexes. The trouble is often simply a case of sperm getting lost in the fluff when cocks do not quite 'hit target'. This is also true of Orpingtons and some other very fluffy breeds.

## Rosecomb

A very ancient breed, as referred to earlier, Rosecombs have become one of the favourites of expert exhibitors. Black is the most popular colour as it gives the best contrast with the birds' large, circular, white ear lobes and red combs, faces and wattles. Blues and Whites have been the only other colours standardised in Britain, but recently many other colours have started appearing here from Holland and Germany.

Rosecombs will live healthily and can be bred from as long as any other breed, but they can only be shown for one year. The white lobes become discoloured and go droopy. Also the white spreads onto the face, especially around the eyes.

Silver Sebright male. (Katie Thear)     Lemon Millefleur Booted bantam. (Katie Thear)

The new colour varieties have smaller lobes than Blacks, and so are less trouble and keep their looks for longer.

Apart from the lobes they are normal bantams and easy to keep. Their tails are quite large and they have broad feathers with rounded ends, so as with other similar breeds, do not put perches too close to the house walls and use houses of a fair size.

## Sebright

As mentioned in the general history section, these have been bred for two hundred years. Gold and Silver Laced are the two varieties accepted here, with more colour combinations of the laced pattern bred in Europe. Sebrights are well known for being in-bred and infertile, a result of breeders being reluctant to cross strains. The lacing has to be really perfect. No matter how vigorous and fertile a Sebright may be, if the markings are no good, they will not be kept by a specialist breeder.

Sebrights are a 'hen-feathered' breed, that is, the cocks do not have pointed neck and saddle hackle feathers or normal cock tail feathers, like other breeds. This is due to a gene affecting hormones in the skin and feather follicles. It is nothing to do with their infertility problems. Another unusual feature which Sebrights should have, is dark skinned combs and faces. The females often have correct dark purple heads, but males almost always have bright red combs, although the best have dark skin around their dark eyes.

They should have short backs with a little of the style of a fan-tail pigeon. Some Golds recently imported from Europe are right, most others are very long backed with no trace of this style. This is a result of Sebright breeders concentrating on the lacing for many years.

Clearly Sebrights are very beautiful, but not really suitable for beginners. I suggest you start with Laced Wyandottes instead and leave Sebrights until you are more experienced.

A family group of Black Booted bantams. (Katie Thear)

# The Rare Breeds

In parenthesis, after each breed name (below) is the section it would move to if ever it became popular enough to have a separate breed club. Only keep a Rare Breed if you are sure that you will be breeding from them as it is irresponsible not to do so. Some of them are bred by five or less people with a total UK population of less than 100 birds. If you happen to live near a keen breeder then you will have no trouble buying at least his or her breeds, but it may be that the nearest flock of the type you would like to try is 100 miles or more away.

## Andalusian (Light)

There is only one colour variety, Blue with black lacing. Ideally the ground colour should be a bright even bluish-grey and the lacing sharp and crisp. This ideal is seldom seen, partly because only half the chicks are blue laced. Black and Splash (white with some blue and/or black feathers) chicks are a by-product of any blue breed. Breeding expectations are as follows:

> Blue x Blue gives 50% Blue, 25% Splash, 25% Black
> Blue x Black gives 50% Blue, 50% Black
> Blue x Splash gives 50% Blue, 50% Splash
> Black x Splash gives 100% Blue

The last mating is obviously the most productive for Blues, but you cannot see how good the lacing of the chicks might be.

Black and Splash Andalusians cannot be shown, but are still useful for breeding. Their lacing genes are unknown, but the birds with good combs, lobes and body shape can still be selected. All these features are typical Mediterranean breed type. It is the difficulty of breeding good ones that has kept these very beautiful birds rare.

Porcelaine Booted bantams. One of the hens is showing signs of broodiness. (Katie Thear)

## Booted (True Bantam)

This old breed virtually died out in Britain sometime between 1900 and 1914. The birds seen here now have come from the Netherlands, hence their Dutch name Sabelpoot is often used. At least one breeder claims to have an old British strain.

In shape they are very similar to Barbu d'Uccles, but without the beard, and perhaps a touch taller and slimmer overall. Having heavily feathered feet, they need special housing and care; so may not be suitable for most beginners. A wide range of colours are bred in the Netherlands and Germany, where they are much more popular. Here you will only find Whites, Blacks, Millefleurs, Porcelaines and Lemon-Millefleurs at present.

## Brakel (Light)

Miniatures of an old Belgian farmyard breed, they are very rare here, with probably less than five breeders. Golds are also standardised, and some large Gold Brakels are bred here, but I have only seen Silver Brakel bantams.

They have medium sized single combs, smallish white ear lobes and typical light breed body shape with quite large tails. Plumage is predominently black and white barred, with clear white necks in hens, and in the necks and saddles of the cocks. This is genetically similar to the Silver Pencilled Hamburgh pattern.

## Friesian (Light)

A hardy breed from the windswept northern part of the Netherlands, large Friesians only weigh from 1.2 to 1.6kg (2¾ to 3½lb) and are often entered in bantam classes at shows by mistake. Friesian bantams are really tiny, 450 to 650gm (16 to 22oz), the same as Rosecombs. Like Brakels, they are typical Light Breeds, active birds needing grassy runs with high fences. Friesians have single combs, white lobes, bluish grey shanks and feet, and they lay lots of white eggs.

Three versions of the Pencilled (as Hamburgh) pattern are standardised, but only one is seen here: Chamois Pencilled. The cocks are clear rich yellow-buff all over except for the tail feathers which are edged with white. Hens are finely marked, in rich yellow-buff and white in an 'ears of wheat' design on all feathers except for the neck, which is clear rich yellow-buff. Ideally their run should be shaded from strong sunlight (by trees or walls) as the colour fades.

## German Langshan (Heavy)

When posing properly, 'Germans' should have a 'wine glass' outline. Long legs provide the stem. The rising angle of the tail and saddle should be symmetrical with the head and neck. Also the line of the breast should be symmetrical with the abdomen. They are topped by fairly small, neat single combs. Blacks, Blues and Whites are the main colours seen here. They have more varieties in Germany, including Birchen and Brown-red.

Long lines of Germans can be seen standing smartly in their cages at the shows. Most people would naturally assume they are a popular breed, and wonder why they are in the Rare section. A look in the catalogue will show that they all come from a small group of keen breeders.

## Houdan (Light)

The 5th edition of *British Poultry Standards* says this is a heavy breed, but it is a mistake. There is only one colour variety, Black with white mottling. They have feathered crests behind unique leaf (also called butterfly) combs. Houdans are another of the breeds with an extra hind toe. The main breeding problem is obtaining an even mix of black and white. Instead they often resemble a White-Crested Black Poland, no doubt showing a shared ancestry.

They are very rare, with probably less than ten flocks worldwide, so there is an urgent need for more breeders.

## Kraienköppe (Light)

This is the German name of a breed which comes from the border areas with the Netherlands. Twentse is the Dutch name. These elegant little bantams are also only bred by a couple of people here, and need more to keep them. There are more breeders in their home countries. Two varieties exist, Gold and Silver. These are the same pattern as Gold and Silver Partridge Dutch.

## Lakenvelder (Light)

This is another Dutch/German border breed. In Germany the name is spelled Lakenfelder. It has a single comb and white lobes, and is another typical light breed-shaped breed. The plumage patterning is a very striking combination of black and white. The neck and tail should be solid black, with some black markings on the wing feathers. The remainder should be clear white. It is not easy to breed. The main fault is white feathers mixed in the neck.

A trio of Lakenvelder bantams. (Katie Thear)

Whether they are perfectly marked or not, these active bantams are good layers, but they need outside grassy runs to keep fit and well.

## Nankin (True Bantam)

Once, two centuries ago, these birds were the common gingery coloured bantam of the countryside. They were used in the development of Gold Sebrights and all the buff and red coloured breeds, but were neglected themselves. When shows started, and breed clubs were formed, there never was a Nankin Club, and Nankins gradually died out.

Originally small, jaunty little birds, most of the few now seen are too big, and lack style. The name is derived from their colour, the same as Nankeen cloth that was once common. The ends of their tails are black. Both single and rose combs are allowed.

## Orloff (Heavy)

The most important part of an Orloff is the head character. They have compact walnut or raspberry combs, short thick beaks, feathered beards and bushy eyebrows. Five colours are standardised, but only one is seen, the Spangled. This is a very irregular version of the Millefleur pattern, with the main ground colour being a rich, dark mahogany. It is also very rare.

## Rumpless Game (Hard Feather)

A tail-less version of Old English Game bantams, Rumpless Modern Game are in the process of being re-made. Both are particularly associated with the Isle of Man. Although there are not many breeders, at least there are lots of normal (tailed) Modern and OEG which can be crossed with in-bred strains of Rumpless. After a few generations of careful selective breeding any initial half formed tailed birds can be eliminated.

## Spanish (Light)

Many breeds have white ear lobes, but only Spanish have completely white faces. Photographs of large Spanish in the 1900 to 1930 period show extraordinary large faces extending well down the neck on some cocks. The large breed was known at least as far back as 1750.

Spanish bantams were first bred about 1880, but died out during World War One. The current stock is a re-make, started by Fred Hams from Kent about 1980. Other breeders, including myself, are continuing with this project, but it will be a few more years before Spanish bantams have white faces as big, in proportion, as the best large fowl. The white skin

A pair of White-Faced Black Spanish bantams. (Katie Thear)

must cover all the face, especially over the eyes and up between the wattles, the two parts most likely to show red. They have single combs, upright on cocks, flopping over on hens. The eyes should be dark to contrast with the face. Otherwise, they are a typical Mediterranean breed shape. Black is the only plumage colour standardised. Blues and Whites have appeared in large Spanish from time to time.

## Sulmtaler (Heavy)
A recent arrival from Austria, there are not many Sulmtalers in Britain. Very much a typical farmyard bantam, these productive little birds should attract more breeders as stock becomes available. Body shape is rounded and compact. They have smallish single combs with a small feathered crest behind. There is only one colour variety: Black-red males with Wheaten females.

## Sumatra (Light)
With their long tails, held horizontally, Sumatras look like exotic pheasants. This impression is enhanced by their having small pea combs and very small wattles, so they look even less like chickens. Two colours are bred: Blue and very glossy Black. The skin of their heads should be dark blue, although some cocks have red combs which is not ideal.

They need large houses with high perches to avoid breaking those tail feathers. When running out on the lawn on a sunny day they look superb. Keep them in when wet, as caked mud wrecks the tails.

## Transylvanian Naked Neck (Heavy)
The name says it all! Their necks should be completely bare, showing bright red skin. Some have a few feathers halfway down the front of the neck, which are often pulled out for showing. Judges count the feather follicles and give first prize to the one which had least feathers before being 'improved'.

They need to be outside as much as possible. Sun and wind keep the necks nice and red, for they can look anaemic if kept in. Close examination of the rest of the bodies of these otherwise apparently normal chickens, shows large areas of bare skin, apart from the main feather tracts.

Large Transylvanian Naked Necks are a very popular table breed in southern Europe and the Middle East. For these regions, commercial Naked Necked broiler strains have recently been developed.

Transylvanian Naked Neck bantams are perfectly hardy for most of England and Wales, but may not survive very exposed situations on hills and moors. In sheltered suburban gardens they will do just fine.

They have normal single combs with a cap of feathers, then the bare neck. The feathers start again across the shoulders and about halfway down the crop. Their tails are medium to long, and are ideally held just above the horizontal. Bantam Transylvanian Naked Necks are very small, considering they are miniatures of a Rare, Heavy breed. There are several colours, with Blacks and Whites being the most popular.

Children and adults with the right sort of sense of humour love them. As an extra treat you can see the food going down when they eat, and day old Transylvanian Naked Neck chicks are amazing.

## Vorwerk (Light)

From Germany, Vorwerks are similar to Lakenvelders but the plumage is black and buff instead of black and white. The same problems in breeding perfectly coloured birds, without an intermingling of colours, apply. Vorwerks are slightly easier to breed. This is another recently arrived breed, so not much stock is available. Large Vorwerks have been here longer and are attracting more breeders.

## Welbar (Light)

These are the Autosexing version of Welsummers. Autosexing breeds have different coloured male and female day-old chicks, for ease of identification; the females are darker. A dozen or so of them were developed at Cambridge by Professor Punnett *et al.* It was thought that they would be useful as commercial breeds, but they were swept aside by the development of hybrids.

Welbars are the most promising of the three Autosexing breeds which have been produced in bantam form because they are attractive birds laying dark brown eggs like Welsummers. Body shape and all other features are exactly like Welsummers except for the addition of the barring gene which changes the plumage to the crele pattern.

Cocks have gold and white, finely barred neck and saddle hackles. The remainder is cuckoo barred shades of grey. Hens have yellow, black and white marked necks, salmon breasts and brown and grey marked backs.

Black Sumatra bantam male. (John Tarren)

## Wybar (Heavy)

This is an autosexing breed based on Wyandottes.

## Rhodebar (Heavy)

This is an autosexing breed based on Rhode Island Reds.

## Yokohama (Light)

These are miniatures of the famous long tailed fowl of Japan. Yokohama bantams do not have tails anywhere near as long as proper Japanese 'O-Naga-Dori'. The world record for these is an extraordinary 12m long tail!

Bantams will get up to 60cm (2ft) long tails. Even this needs a lot of special care. Large houses, high perches and an obsessive attention to cleanliness and every detail of management are essential.

A lot of people keep Yokohamas in normal garden or smallholding conditions where they will still be very pretty, but never reach their full potential. Tail feathers will get broken. There is no shortage of stock for Yokohamas can be found at almost every poultry auction. Exhibitors prepared to take the time and trouble to keep them in feather perfect condition are much rarer.

There is a wide range of feeders and drinkers available, for inside and outside use. They are made of galvanised metal or plastic. Here, the Black Red Yokohama has been provided with a feeder with a weather-protection hood. The gravity-fed drinker is at the back. (Katie Thear)

Drinkers on perforated stands help to keep the surrounding area dry.

Suspended greens are useful in helping to prevent boredom which can lead to feather-pecking.

# Feeding

*Cleanliness in feeding is essential to the growth and well-being of all stock,*
*and this applies most emphatically to chickens.*
(D.F. Suttie, 1929)

Many old poultry books have chapters on feeding, including many recipes for home mixed mashes and corn mixtures. Today we just go to our local animal feed supplier and buy bags of chick crumbs, grower's and layer's pellets.

These are designed for quick maturing and high producing commercial hybrid layers. It often recommends on the bags that chick crumbs should be fed from day old to 8 weeks, followed by the grower's pellets until 18 or 20 weeks of age when the hybrids start laying. They will produce up to 300 eggs over the next year. Layer's pellets include about 3% limestone flour to make all those egg shells.

## Chick crumbs

Bantams, especially some in-bred strains of pure breeds, are much slower in maturing and will not lay anywhere near as many eggs. Also, breeding cock birds do not make eggshells! Bantam pullets do not start laying until they are at least 35 weeks old. In-bred strains are less efficient at absorbing nutrients than hybrids or crossbreds, so these chicks need to be kept on chick crumbs for at least 12 weeks. Many breeders use chick crumbs for longer still, particularly for the very tiny breeds which do not eat much.

Most brands of chick crumbs and grower's pellets contain drugs called *Coccidiostats* to prevent the birds catching Coccidiosis. This is a protozoan disease causing haemorrhages in the intestines. There are several species of Coccidia, each of which has its target part of the gut and a very specific age of bird affected. Blood in the droppings, frequently followed by the death of the bird, are the main symptoms. The life cycle of Coccidial protozoans can be effectively broken by resting the ground between flocks and ensuring that litter in houses and runs is changed frequently.

For those with strong feelings about 'additives', some non-medicated feeds are available. I do not recommend them, having lost a lot of chicks to this horrible disease over the years. Even with the Coccidiostats some chicks will be lost if there is a virulent strain of the disease. Free range birds are more likely to catch Coccidiosis and many other diseases are carried by wild birds and their droppings. However, there is less chance of getting it if the land to which the birds have access is changed regularly and damp areas of litter are cleared away, as referred to earlier and in the *Housing* chapter. It is also worth remembering that as most bantams will not be producing eggs for a comparatively long time, they will usually have stopped taking rations with additives before eggs are available for eating. Chickens are most at risk from Coccidiosis during the growing period.

## Layer's pellets

Layer's pellets are a complete food, providing all the nutrients required in a balanced formula. As referred to earlier, they are more geared to commercial layers than home flocks, but are still the best basic ration for bantams. An individual would be hard-pressed to produce his own mix in the right balance. Free-range and organic mixes are also available, without the additives included in standard rations.

Ornamental fowl pellets are also available from specialist suppliers. These are suitable for bantams and for any poultry which are to be exhibited, and where aspects such as feather bloom and tip-top condition are important.

## Mixed corn

Mixed corn is usually three quarters wheat with a quarter cut or 'kibbled' maize. This can be given in small quantities to growers after about three months. Do not give much at this stage or it will dilute the Coccidiostat in the grower's ration.

Bags of ready mixed corn can be bought from your regular feed supplier. It may be cheaper to buy the wheat from a local farmer and then just buy the maize from the shop. Maize is low in protein and is fattening, but the yellow pigments in it help to give good coloured egg yolks and bright coloured shanks and feet on yellow legged breeds. Without it, the feet will be a pale creamy shade and will not win that cup. Maize should not comprise more than 10% of the diet.

Adult bantams can be fed about 60% layer's pellets and 40% mixed corn. They are not going to lay as much as the hybrids the pellets were designed for, and the cock birds will be better for having less limestone flour.

## Grit

There are two types of grit, which perform different functions. Oystershell grit is soluble in the gut and is used to provide the correct balance of calcium and phosphorus for making eggshells. Some hens, especially older birds, have a tendency to lay soft-shelled or porous-shelled eggs, despite the limestone flour in a layer's ration. Oystershell helps to combat this.

Flint grit is insoluble and lodges in the gizzard to grind the food like small grindstones in a mill. Free ranging bantams will probably find enough small stones themselves, but housed birds will need to be given flint grit. Eviscerating chickens became a popular job during the 1849 California Gold Rush for apparently the birds picked up gold nuggets during their free-ranging activities!

## Breeder's ration

Special breeder's pellets and even high protein pheasant rations are available from some outlets. They are very good, especially for tiny breeds with small appetites.

Breeder's rations also provide the necessary proteins and trace elements for breeding birds, otherwise their progeny may suffer from deficiency diseases. Chicks born with curly toes and clubbed ends to their down feathers, for example, are the result of Vitamin $B_2$ (Riboflavin) deficiency in the parents. Similarly, a deficiency of Vitamin D in the parents' diet leads to an inability to metabolize calcium and phosphorus in the chicks so they hatch with splayed legs or twisted breastbones.

Breeder's rations are now available in small quantities from specialist suppliers, and it is worth feeding these from winter onwards to birds whose eggs are to be incubated in the spring. They contain omega oils and linseed in addition to other nutrients, and are available as small-sized pellets which are just right for bantams.

## Greens

Free-ranging birds will obtain a certain proportion of greens from their foraging activities. These help to provide some of the minerals in their diet. Kitchen garden greens can also be suspended in a run to provide interest and prevent boredom which might otherwise lead to feather-pecking. They should be regarded as an addition to the normal diet, rather than a replacement to it, otherwise digestive problems may occur.

## Water

Clean, fresh water in a clean drinker is essential at all times. Both drinkers and feeders should be cleaned regularly to prevent the build-up of moulds and other pathogens that can cause disease. Galvanised metal containers are better for outside use, while plastic is suitable for inside. They can be suspended or placed on stands to prevent litter contaminating the water, and also to keep the surrounding area free of damp.

## Predators and vermin

The importance of keeping poultry feed in rodent-proof containers and not leaving any lying around, cannot be stressed too strongly. Although you may not see them, both rats and mice are likely to be in the vicinity and can smell bird droppings as well as feed stuffs.

Mice are not likely to be a problem to birds, but they can be a nuisance if they get into the food storage area. Both traps and a good cat can be effective in dealing with them. Rats, on the other hand, are not only a danger to chicks but spread disease and can contaminate feed. If you see one rat, or even evidence of their droppings, you can be certain that there are several around. Take action to block any entrances to the poultry buildings, clear away rubbish lying nearby and cut down brambles or long grass which may be concealing their 'runs'. Traps are available from suppliers, or rat poison such as *Sorex* can be put down. Make sure that it is placed well out of reach of children, domestic pets, wild birds and the poultry.

Alternatively, you can call in the local Pest Control Officer from the Environmental Services department of the local council.

Finally, the fox is adept at finding his way into poultry runs. The only way to protect the birds is to make sure that they are locked in at night, and that the perimeter walls are high enough to deter him. Electric poultry netting is also effective.

# Some examples of housing

Above: A *Domestic Fowl Trust* wheeled, movable unit with house at one end and shelter for a feeder and drinker at the other. The run can be opened from the top.

Above: A movable house and run suitable for a breeding trio of bantams.

Left: A small house and run with handles for moving the unit. A nest box with access from the outside makes it easier to collect the eggs. *Photo: Littleacres.*

A movable house and integral run, equipped with carrying handles. These Frizzles have access to a grassed area in the vegetable garden.

*Photo: Forsham Cottage Arks.*

# Housing

*When hens go to roost on the beams of the shed,*
*Light thine own candle and prepare thee for bed.*
(Tusser, 1651)

Some beginners may imagine that they will have just one bantam house with a grassy run. More than this will be needed if you are to keep and breed bantams for any length of time. When hens go broody they need somewhere separate to sit undisturbed by the other hens. When the chicks hatch, the family will need a secure, dry house or cage in a shed for two months or so, followed by somewhere larger for the growing youngsters. They cannot be reared in with the adults.

Even those single minded enough to keep just one variety will gradually build up their flock over a few years. Any serious breeder will want to have some 'spares' in case of deaths, cocks proving to be infertile or hens laying eggs of not good enough quality to be hatchable. It is unlikely that good quality replacements can be easily bought to fit in exactly with a strain which has been carefully bred for some years.

Before you buy or build much housing, or get many bantams, it is best to have a clear overall plan in mind. If possible, visit some experienced breeders with the same (or similar) varieties to those you have in mind. The secretary of your nearest local poultry club should be able to suggest someone to visit. As the *Breeds* part of this book makes clear, breeds with feathered feet, long tails and other features need housing to suit their needs.

Beginners usually start by trying several breeds and eventually specialise in one or two. Life will be easier if the initial choice is from a group of similar sized breeds. A group of assorted tiny *True Bantam* breed youngsters can be reared together, but they will be bullied if there are growers of the larger breeds of bantams present.

There are several basic types of housing from small movable arks to large sheds divided into pens. All have their uses and most breeders will have several types after a few years. For most people, with some basic DIY ability, the best value for money is to buy one or more garden sheds and do the necessary conversions. If after some years you decide bantam keeping is not for you, the sheds can be converted back for other uses. Purpose made poultry houses usually have very low roofs and are not so adaptable. Standard garden sheds are often on 'Special Offer', and so will probably be cheaper.

Most established breeders will have a fair sized penning room, with a bank of cages of various sizes for broody hens, hens with chicks, show training and housing spare cockerels. Proper penning rooms usually also include storage space for poultry food, carrying boxes, etc.

A movable house with mesh panels arranged around it for a run. If necessary, the top can be covered with mesh to provide overhead protection. Solid wood panels can be placed along the bottom to act as a windbreak, or to stop cocks fighting where there are adjoining runs.

# Penning area

Beginners will not need a penning room, just one or two cages fitted high up in your converted shed houses. Make a shelf about 75cm (30 in) from front to back, and about 90cm (3ft) above the floor. The shelf can run along one side or at the end of the shed, as you think appropriate. Each cage should be about 90-120cm (3-4 ft) long, so the number of cages will depend on the size of the shed. The fronts of the cages should be of a small enough gauge of wire mesh to keep in day old chicks when the cage is used as a nursery.

These high cages leave the floor clear for adult birds or older growers. A 180 x 240cm (6ft x 8ft) shed can be divided to give two 180 x 120cm (6ft x 4ft) pens. The partition should be plywood up to 90cm (3ft) high, as cocks will probably try to fight through mesh, even if they are docile breeds. The top half of the partition should be wire netting, with the dividing door the same. There should be a 15 cm (6in) board running along the floor below the door. If the door goes down to the floor it will be difficult to open because of the shavings covering the floor.

# House fixtures and fittings

## Perches

For most breeds, perches should be about 60cm (2ft) above the floor, higher for long tailed breeds and lower for the heaviest breeds such as Indian Game and feather footed breeds. They need to be about 5cm (2in) wide with the top edges rounded off. Narrow perches can cause dented breast-bones. On young birds the breast-

Home-made houses and runs with a flock of bantam Marans in the foreground. (Katie Thear)

bone is still mostly soft cartilage and is easily deformed. It is best to keep young-sters sleeping on the floor as long as possible. When you see them trying to perch up on any improbable surface you will have to give in and give them a perch, pref-erably an extra wide one to start with.

Ideally, perches should slot into brackets rather than be nailed into place. Thus it is easier to check for Red Mite or to take out the perch when the house or pen is used for rearing young stock.

## Pop-holes

These are the small bantam sized doors fitted to allow the birds out to their grass runs. They should be at least 30cm (12in) square. You may be starting with a small breed, but could change to something larger later, so the pop-holes might as well be big enough to cater for all likely eventualities. Have either sliding doors, or if the house is raised off the ground, doors which are hinged at the bottom and open down to form a ramp.

## Nest-boxes

Commercially made poultry houses are usually fitted with built in nest-boxes. These are fine for most layers but are not ideal for long-tailed breeds. If you are converting a shed or building from scratch, I would recommend removable nests. Plastic five gallon drums laid on their side, with a hole cut in the side and a brick in front as a 'doorstep' are best of all. They are washable, have smooth, rounded inside surfaces to preserve tail feathers, and when a hen goes broody, she can be moved in the nest in which she has happily settled to a quiet cage to do her sitting in peace. These drums can be found at many factories and farms. They were originally containers for detergents, etc.

If your scrounging skills are not well developed, then strong cardboard boxes are a good alternative. They can be replaced when dirty and tatty and so are more hygienic than permanent nests.

Hens like to feel as hidden away as possible when laying and sitting, a natural instinct from their jungle-fowl ancestors, so the nests in the darkest corners will be their favourites.

## Warmth versus ventilation

Bantams prefer to be at a comfortable temperature, neither too hot nor too cold. An apparently comfortable house in the morning, during mid-summer, may become unbearably hot in the afternoon when you are away at work. The best plan is to have all windows completely removable, with wire netting over the space.

A converted garden shed will probably need an extra window cut out, and will be brighter if the inside walls are painted with white emulsion.

## Floor covering

Floors should be covered with some sort of litter to dry out and absorb the droppings. Feather-footed and Japanese bantams will need to be cleaned out regularly, but other breeds can be left a surprisingly long time, as long as the house is dry. If the drinking water container is tipped over then the wet patch must be cleaned out straight away.

Woodshavings, bought in compacted plastic covered bales, is the best material. If you can get shavings free from a local carpentry business, then only take white, softwood shavings from untreated wood. Hardwood (red) shavings have choking dust and are no use at all.

Straw is cheap, sometimes free, and is suitable for adults of the larger breeds, but tends to mat down and get wet when used for bantams which are too small or inactive to scratch it about. When well scratched, straw soon breaks down to chaff, which is better. It is possible to buy bags of finely chopped and clean straw for litter but it is fairly expensive.

## Run fencing

The ideal is to have the bottom 60cm (2ft) as solid wood, with 120cm (4ft) of wire netting above, giving a total height of 1.8m (6ft). The solid part acts as a windbreak and prevents cocks in adjoining runs from fighting. Even docile breeds of cocks will fight to some extent, and often do more damage to themselves on the wire netting itself than they do to each other.

Perimeter fencing must be fox and badger proof. Both predators will try to dig their way in, so some buried, heavy duty weldmesh may be needed. Many badgers lead blameless lives, but if one does get a taste for chicken, they are very powerful animals which can, and do, break into runs and houses.

Broody coop and run for a hen and chicks. (Walner)

Remember a lot of foxes live right in our large cities, and urban foxes seem to be more determined than their country cousins. Do not fit a wooden top rail to the fencing. This will be a useful perch for escaping bantams and intruding foxes. Wobbly wire netting is not as inviting.

## Run layout

Bantams need time out on grass, not mud! The larger and more active breeds can soon strip a run down to bare earth. If space is limited it is probably better to have houses large enough to keep them in, perhaps with covered aviaries attached, and then have one larger grass run for two or more houses which the bantams use in turn. Better two days a week on grass than seven on bare earth.

Larger scale breeders have their houses near a paved path so they do not need to walk right across each run. This saves time and the grass.

Pop-holes need to be big enough for comfort and to allow for future occupants. Here, a ramp is provided for the Partridge Dutch bantams. (Katie Thear)

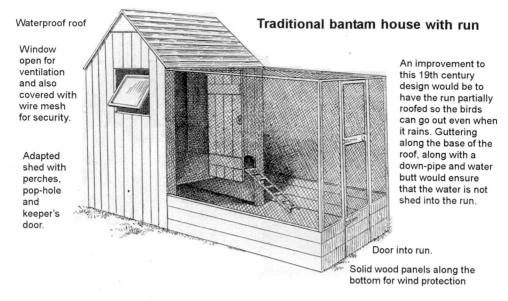

**Traditional bantam house with run**

Waterproof roof

Window open for ventilation and also covered with wire mesh for security.

Adapted shed with perches, pop-hole and keeper's door.

An improvement to this 19th century design would be to have the run partially roofed so the birds can go out even when it rains. Guttering along the base of the roof, along with a down-pipe and water butt would ensure that the water is not shed into the run.

Door into run.

Solid wood panels along the bottom for wind protection

# Traditional bantam houses

• The house should be large enough to keep the birds shut in when necessary, with a minimum floor area about 1 sq. metre (9sq.ft)
• Creosote second-hand houses before use and then leave to dry and air completely before allowing the birds access. They are sometimes advertised in local papers.
• Is it light enough? Some designs are very dark and stuffy. Choose one with a large window.
• Is the door large enough for you to clean out the house comfortably, or catch your bantams? These houses can be made more accessible if stood on some concrete blocks. All this is especially important if the bantam keeper is not very agile.
• There are many designs on the market; some may suit your layout better than others. Are the doors, windows, nest-boxes, etc, on the right sides to suit the paths and general layout of your garden? Some manufacturers will produce 'right-handed' and 'left-handed' versions of their designs to order.

# Arks

These are small houses with attached runs which are moved every day to fresh grass. Do not buy the smallest models unless they are intended just for odd cockerels or a hen with chicks. Choose designs with a fair sized house part, and with a partly covered run to give shelter from the weather. Those with wheels or carrying handles are easier to move. Arks are safer where foxes are a problem and are the best option if you have a paddock which you also use for sheep or geese.

Some breeders use arks to give time outside for birds otherwise kept in. Farmers and smallholders with open barns can move their bantam arks under shelter for the winter.

# Breeding

*Hens like to lay when they see an egg.* (Traditional saying)

## Breeding systems

So, you buy a trio of bantams and breed some more from them. What next? Most people have heard of 'in-breeding', 'line breeding' and similar terms but have only a hazy idea of their meaning. Also, societal taboos of incest are carried over into livestock breeding, not necessarily appropriately.

### In-breeding

In-breeding or maintaining a closed flock keeps a high level of genetic uniformity. You pretty much know what you are going to get from a closed flock: more of the same. Following the old engineer's saying, *"If it ain't broke don't fix it!"*, success-ful exhibitors are reluctant to introduce unrelated stock into their strains because they fear, correctly, that although the birds so bred may be more vigorous and fertile than their in-bred birds, they will be much less perfectly marked or much too big to be an acceptable show bantam.

In-breeding *depression* or in-breeding *degeneration* is the inevitable result of many generations of close in-breeding. It is where there has been a great deal of mating between close relatives. Most breeders of Sebrights, for example, have to contend with poor egg production and fertility, and the few chicks hatched are very delicate. But, a Sebright is a very precise bird. The lacing of the feathers, the comb, and the size and type of the bird all have to be correct, otherwise it is not worth having. Luckily, some European bred Sebrights are now available here, so our breed-ers at last have some suitable fresh stock to use. Even so, I am sure they will wing-tab and/or leg-ring all chicks very carefully so they know which are original strains and which are from the new stock.

Most of the harmful genes causing problems are *recessive*, as distinct from *domi-nant*. In other words, they tend not to manifest unless they are inherited from both parents. In populations where birds (or animals or people) which are not related are producing young, then it is very bad luck indeed if a mating pair has the same harmful, recessive genes. The harmful genes of each parent are usually prevented from operating by the good, dominant genes of the other. In closed populations there is a greatly increased risk that both parents will be carrying the same harmful, recessive genes (but masked and therefore undetectable), thus producing 25% with the faulty genes operating, and a further 50% with a single faulty, recessive gene to carry on to future generations.

## Closed flocks

Closed flocks can be perpetuated for an extended period - even decades or more - by keeping as large a flock as possible, and with good organisation, taking care to mate cousins rather than siblings. In an ideal arrangement, as might be employed by a commercial operation, there would be six or eight breeding pens of a strain, with the cockerels from pen A being bred to the pullets from pen B, and so on. Hobbyist breeders will usually have to make do with three or four pens, and keep as many cockerels as possible in order to maintain as wide a genetic pool as possible within the strain. This is why most of the famous names in our hobby are specialists. They understand why it is necessary to keep a large flock of nearly identical birds. This is often lost on beginners who, after visiting an expert, are probably thinking, *"That was a bit boring. I'd rather have lots of different kinds, with just a few of each"*.

## Line breeding

Line breeding is a form of in-breeding where maximum use is made of one out-standing individual. The rotational mating of a large, closed flock is what is necessary to keep a very good strain going. Line breeding is what went on before. Imagine if you have bought a trio, have bred a good bunch and one of the cockerels has won some *Best in Show* awards. The obvious next step is to breed from him, and the following year to breed from him and his daughters. If he lives that long, continue with his grand-daughters and great grand-daughters. You will gradually be building up the numbers so that by the time the original champion goes off to the great free-range in the sky, you will have enough birds to switch to the rotational system above. This, with careful selection and some luck will be the foundation of a succession of future champions. The aim of breeding for the shows should not be a Holy Grail style quest for the perfect specimen, but rather many years of regularly being 'in the cards' at the shows.

## Out-breeding

Out-breeding or out-crossing is where very unrelated strains are bred together. It may be done to rejuvenate an overly in-bred strain, as illustrated in the Sebright example referred to earlier. In this case, after the outcross, it is then back to in-breeding as normal for the next few years. Where the production of utility birds is concerned, it will be used regularly. If you were thinking of producing 'laying bantams' for sale, most likely with Araucanas, Marans, Welsummers or Welbars, then the best method would be to develop two separate in-bred strains of whichever breed it is. The productive layers would be strain crosses between these two lines. This is the method used to make commercial 'hybrids'.

Maximum *hybrid vigour* is only obtained in $F_1$ stock from in-bred parents. ($F_1$ stock is a hybrid strain from the careful crossings of pure-bred parents of the same breed, giving uniformity and vigour). Quite a large scale operation is needed to do this properly, with very careful record keeping so that the parentage of every egg and chick is known. This is why no-one, as far as I am aware, produces utility bantams.

Silver Campine male and female. At present there is no bantam form of this breed but it is one to consider for miniaturisation. Pencilled Hamburgh or Brakel would be suitable as a starting point cross with the smallest available Campine. (Katie Thear)

## Upgrading

Upgrading has most often been used in 'third world' countries to improve indigenous stocks, in so far as the local climatic and disease conditions allow. Highly productive American and European poultry (or other livestock) often sicken and die in the tropics, but crosses of three-quarter breds with local breeds give a practical compromise between productivity and survivability. For hobbyist poultry keepers, this process is used as an emergency measure with nearly extinct, rare breeds. In the 1960s, poultry breeder Rex Woods bought most of the surviving large Spanish and crossed them with Minorcas. This was followed by more back-crosses to Spanish, to produce a vigorous population of nearly pure White-faced Spanish.

## Cross-breeding

Cross-breeding is the mating of one pure breed with another. It is not normally done in bantam breeding, unless in an emergency (as with the Spanish example above), or when a new breed is being made. As there are already more than enough recognised varieties for the world's bantam breeders to keep going, it is not something that is generally advocated. In many cases, there is no point as it is highly likely that the breed clubs would not recognise a new creation.

There are a few varieties of bantam which would be acceptable as they already exist as large fowl, but have not yet been bantamised. Examples to consider include Cuckoo, Dark, Red and White Dorkings, Gold and Silver Campines, Ixworths, La Fleche or Modern Langshans.

Old English Game bantams can become very tame, as breeder Mr G.L.Talbot demonstrates.

In the case of the Dorkings, the initial cross would be between under-sized large Dorkings of whichever colour is to be made, and Silver Grey Dorking bantams, the only colour currently existing. After about five years of breeding many, and just breeding from the best, the result should be reasonable but not yet perfect specimens.

The same process, one or two initial crosses followed by years producing large numbers of chicks from which only a small proportion will be used for breeding, will be used for the other suggested 'new' breeds. In all cases, one parent will be the smallest available specimen of the large breed. For the other parents, I suggest Brakels and Pencilled Hamburghs for Campines, White Sussex, Jubilee Game and White Ko-Shamo for Ixworths. For La Fleche, use Black Minorcas first, followed by Black Rosecombs. Rosecombs are too small to mate with a large La Fleche.

In the case of Modern Langshans you may not be able to find any large ones, so start with a Croad Langshan bantam x Black Modern Game mating.

As all these projects involve producing a lot of unwanted birds, be prepared to eat a lot of cockerels, and have a lot of cross-bred pullets to sell as layers.

The genetics of poultry will have to be studied in depth. You will need an up-to-date book, for much has been discovered recently. Dr Clive Carefoot, in particular, has proved that a lot of the old text books were wrong on the partridge, pencilled and double-laced patterns.

# Successful Hatchings

*Incubation may be either a success or a failure, according to
the manner in which it is carried out.* (Will Hooley)

## Internal egg quality

An egg contains all the nutrients available to the developing embryo. They can fail
to hatch, or die shortly after hatching, if something is lacking. Bantams and pure
breed large fowl do not lay as many eggs as commercial hybrids, so in that respect
there should be no problem as each egg should be of good quality. However, many
of our old breeds are very in-bred, reducing the metabolic efficiency of the hens.
Black and lavender coloured chicks often suffer from 'clubbed down'. The downy
feathers fail to open out and appear as little lumps on the chicks instead of the
normal fluffy coat. These pigments use a lot of Riboflavin, one of the B-complex
vitamins, so a dietary supplement may be needed.

Special breeder's pellets, with extra protein and vitamins, can be bought from
some suppliers. Pheasant rations are also used by some. These have much higher
protein levels than bantams really need, but if mixed corn (lower protein) is being
fed, then one will balance the other.

## Broody hens

When a hen goes broody she will stay sitting in her nest all day. If approached she
will react defensively, fluffing up her feathers and giving a strangled type of com-
plaining noise. Leave her where she is for a few days until she is really settled.
Continue to collect any eggs you wish to incubate, for you do not want chicks hatching
over several days. Keep the hen interested with something else: some eggs marked
with a felt tipped pen to identify them as those you do not want to incubate, or
some dummy eggs such as golf balls, will do.

One evening move her, in her nest, into a movable box or plastic drum. If it is a
fixed nest box you will have to prepare another nest box and very gently move her
to it. Either way the broody must be in a separate area with enough space for her to
get in and out, eat, drink and pass droppings. For the first night she must be shut in
the nest with a suitable sized piece of weldmesh or plywood.

After another couple of days, when you are sure she is settled in, remove whatever she has been sitting on and put the eggs to be incubated underneath her. This is
best done in the evening. Write a card with the date started and details of which
breed the eggs are, and pin it on the cage. This is particularly important if you have
several broodies.

Broodies do go rather pale in the face during the sitting period. They are also,
literally, a sitting target for red mite, and it is difficult to tell the difference between

73

a normal broody's paler face, and extra paleness caused by mite. Spray the nest with mite-killer before incubation starts and a couple more times during the process. This is best done when the hen is off the nest, eating.

A Silver Duckwing Yokohama bantam hen sitting on and brooding a clutch of eggs. (Katie Thear)

# Incubators

If intending to use an incubator, buy a good one with automatic turning, and follow the instructions. Models with electronic temperature recording and control are better than older or cheaper types. Also some incubators have internal fans to give a more even heat distribution. These are more expensive but better if affordable.

A common question is: *'What if there is a power cut?'*. The best option is to cover the incubator with a blanket to hold the heat in and hope it does not last very long. Hens go off the nest to feed every day, so embryos are adapted to cope with some cooling. Newly hatched chicks have at least 24 hours worth of yolk inside their bodies, so do not need to be taken out of the incubator as soon as their feathers have fluffed up. Anyway it is better for the unhatched chicks if the incubator is not opened at this critical time. When the main group of chicks is removed, take out the empty shells as well, as they can cap over unhatched eggs.

# Avoiding problems with hatching

It is disappointing for all the family when, after three weeks of anticipation, very few or no chicks arrive. Here are some pointers to help:

## • The right number of hens to each cock?

Bantams are usually sold in trios of a cock with two hens. With the feather footed breeds, small breeds like Sebrights and heavy weights like Indian Game, two hens will be enough. More vigorous breeds, Sussex for example, will be better with more hens. Just two may have a rough time. Any extra bantam hens will do, preferably ones which lay a different coloured egg so the correct eggs can be identified for hatching.

### • Bored cock bird?

It can happen! If you have two cocks for each group of hens, keeping the spare in a raised cage in the house where he can see the hens but not get to them will make him really keen. Every few days, swap the cocks. Thus both will keep working.

### • Early season infertility

There is direct scientific evidence that cold temperatures reduce the efficiency of testes and ovaries.

An incubator, especially one with up-to-date controls and an egg turning facility, is useful when a broody hen is not available. (Curfew)

The optimum temperature for breeding in both sexes is 19°C (66°F). To be more down to earth about it, one breeder memorably said, *"If you were out in a cold muddy field all day, you wouldn't feel like it either."*

Exhibitors try to breed some chicks early in the year so they will be ready for showing in October and November. Breeding stock is kept in warm sheds, preferably with lighting to give longer 'days' to ensure fertile eggs.

### • Unexpected crossbred chicks?

Many people run all their birds together over winter, only putting them in separate breeding groups in the spring. They may not know that sperm can live inside hens for up to three weeks. After this time, and after seven days in with their designated cock, most will be fertile by him. Putting them together earlier can sometimes be successful, as the fresher sperm will be more vigorous than the older sperm, but this is not guaranteed. Also, are your run fences high enough? Sometimes a bird will become quite determined to reach the object of his or her desire.

### • Clean conditions

Eggs have anti-bacterial defence mechanisms but very dirty and damp conditions can overcome them and make the eggs go rotten, a good reason to avoid bantams coming into too much contact with mud. Washing eggs helps, but much better is if they never get dirty. However, washing eggs that are to be incubated, in warm water with an egg sanitant in it, does reduce the incidence of disease and is recommended.

### • Collect eggs daily

This is both to help keep them clean and in winter to avoid getting them frozen. A frozen egg will never hatch. Ideal storage conditions are provided by a cool room, not the refrigerator.

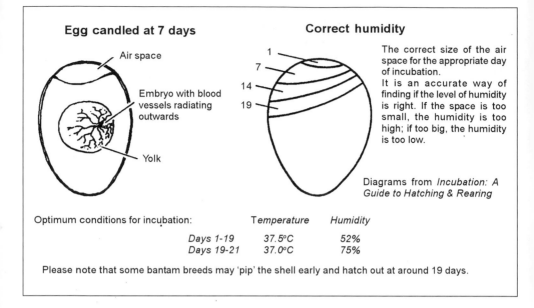

**Egg candled at 7 days**

- Air space
- Embryo with blood vessels radiating outwards
- Yolk

**Correct humidity**

1
7
14
19

The correct size of the air space for the appropriate day of incubation.

It is an accurate way of finding if the level of humidity is right. If the space is too small, the humidity is too high; if too big, the humidity is too low.

Diagrams from *Incubation: A Guide to Hatching & Rearing*

Optimum conditions for incubation:

| | Temperature | Humidity |
|---|---|---|
| Days 1-19 | 37.5°C | 52% |
| Days 19-21 | 37.0°C | 75% |

Please note that some bantam breeds may 'pip' the shell early and hatch out at around 19 days.

Eggs go dormant once laid until proper incubation is started. Many beginners think they should be kept warm all the time if they are to be incubated. No, this will shorten their viable life. If stored at the ideal temperature range of 10 - 15°C (40-50°F) eggs can be kept for up to ten days before incubation is started. (Remember that wild pheasants lay an egg a day until they have about a dozen. They will be out and about feeding until they start sitting).

## • Only incubate viable eggs

Do not try to hatch odd shaped, cracked, porous shelled (they feel rough), double yolked or other duds. Egg size, shape and colour varies from breed to breed. Generally a 'typical' egg will be best. This is very important for Araucanas, Marans and Welsummers where egg shell colours are vital breed characteristics.

Egg size is related to final body size. The bigger the egg, the bigger the chick, the bigger the fully grown bird. Those breeds of bantam which are commonly too big can be reduced by selecting smaller eggs for hatching. Hamburgh bantams are frequently only very slightly smaller than large Hamburghs.

## • Get into the habit of recording

Write, in pencil, the date, breed and group of all eggs as you collect them. Most breeders develop their own shorthand or code for this. This is even more important if you have several pens of one variety. It may be that all the eggs which are infertile (or are fertile but fail to hatch) come from one house.

## • Keep full records of all eggs incubated

Records should include all the eggs, whether they are from an incubator or from under a broody hen. Break open all unhatched eggs. Were they infertile? Were they fertile, but died in the first few days of incubation? Did the embryos die at some later stage? Some make it as far as 'pipping' or cracking the shell, but then die. These are all clues to the cause of any problems.

If you are going to be breeding quite a lot of bantams it is worth buying a specialist reference book such as *Incubation: A Guide to Hatching & Rearing* or *The Incubation Book*, for full details of this complex process.

## • Candling eggs

After the seventh day of incubation the embryo will be visible if a torch is shone through the egg. Do this at night. Hold the egg between your fingers so that your hands cover the torch except for the light coming through the egg. Try this with a fresh egg before you start on the eggs being incubated.

- Clear (infertile) eggs look the same as fresh eggs, with just a faint yellowish area; the yolk.

- Healthy developing embryos show up as a dark spot on the yolk, plus a network of arteries around the egg to draw in air and nutrients. (See diagram).

- Early dead germs show as a 'blood ring'. The network of arteries has collapsed, usually into one red line around the middle of the egg.

This job must be done, and all duds thrown out as they rob heat from developing embryos, and may become rotten and explode. Nasty! Do not worry about the eggs getting cold for a few minutes while you are doing the candling. It will be no worse than a hen getting off to eat, which they do every day.

# Chick rearing

Incubator hatched chicks will need to be reared under a heat lamp. For small groups an ordinary 100 watt light bulb will do, but it must be the screw fitting type and in a ceramic holder, the same sort sold for infra-red bulbs. Larger numbers of chicks (50+) will need an infra-red light, ideally a 'hard glass' one. Switch on when the first egg pips (The first little crack in an egg shell.). This gives at least 24 hours for the chick rearing box to warm up before the chicks will be ready to come out of the incubator.

Set up the light in a large cardboard box, one with a floor area 75 x 90cm (30 x 36ins) or larger. Those originally for lawnmowers or larger domestic appliances are suitable. To start with, cover the box floor with hessian sacking or other rough textured material. Shavings will be added after a week or so, but day-olds without a mother hen to teach them will not know the difference between food and shavings. They can kill themselves by eating shavings.

A brooding area set up for the newly hatched chicks. Note how the drinkers are on wire mesh to keep the litter dry and prevent disease. (Katie Thear)

Sprinkle chick crumbs over the floor to start with as the chicks will just be pecking around randomly. After a few days, when they have got the idea, the food can go in a suitable shallow trough or small plastic hopper. Water should be in small size plastic drinkers or shallow bowls and regularly cleaned out.

As the chicks grow, they should be gradually adapted to lower temperatures. Every 7 to 10 days raise the lamp a little. After the first month change to a lower wattage bulb. The chicks will tell you if they are comfortable. If they huddle together under the centre of the lamp, they are too cold. If they are right away from the lamp they are too hot. The ideal is for the chicks to sit in a circle around the lamp. They will be ready to move on to unheated houses from 6 to 8 weeks of age depending on the general weather conditions and the breed of bantam. Some breeds are quicker growing and feathering than others.

One of the positive features of the show scene is the encouragement given to young people to take part. Many of the larger shows have awards specifically for juveniles in their specific classes. (A juvenile is under 16 and over 12). Juniors (under 12) can compete in special classes in front of a judge, when their knowledge is assessed, in addition to the quality of their exhibit.

# Showing

*He struts like a bantam.* (Traditional saying)

Only a small proportion of bantam keepers show their birds. The shows, with the network of local and breed clubs and the governing body, the *Poultry Club of Great Britain*, are nevertheless the core of our hobby. Looking around the world it is clear that our living heritage of old breeds of large fowl, bantams, ducks, geese and turkeys is generally thriving (although some varieties remain very rare) in those countries where there are shows. In other parts of the world there are just a few scattered enthusiasts, despite the millions of poultry keepers.

Most people will visit a few shows before they enter one themselves. When they do finally have a go, it will usually be a smaller local show. It is natural to think that the National Show or the Stafford Show, the two largest, both with about 6,000 birds, will have to wait a few years. If you are going to exhibit one of the very popular varieties, where there will be huge classes, this is a wise choice. Rarer varieties will not have vast classes even at these two shows, so go on, try!

The public normally only see the poultry sections at the summer agricultural shows and assume that must be it. In fact, the main poultry shows are held through the winter. By late October the chicks hatched in early spring will be maturing and some of the old birds will be finishing their moult, so the main show season starts.

You cannot just turn up on the day at poultry shows, as the secretary has a lot of organising to do. The cages are all set up in advance (just bring your birds in a suitable carrying box), and are numbered to suit exactly the number of each breed of large fowl, bantams, etc, which have been entered.

Entry forms and 'schedules' are sent out four to six weeks before the show and entries usually have to be in about ten days before show day. These times are longer for the National and Stafford. Write or telephone the show secretary to get on the mailing list well in advance. As club subscriptions are very nominal amounts, most exhibitors are members of quite a few clubs.

## Show schedules

These contain all the necessary information:

• Show date

• Place of show, often village halls

• Closing date for entries

• The time all birds must be in the cages, normally 9, 9.30 or 10am., and finishing time, usually about 4pm.

• Entry fees. At small shows this is about £1 per bird, and about 30p for egg entries (plate of several matching, etc.) The fees are higher at the big shows.

Giving a bath. Note the position of the fingers which support the bird yet restrain the wings. (Katie Thear)

• The names of the judges. This will not mean much to beginners, but established fanciers will sometimes partly choose which show to attend, depending on the judge. In some breeds there are differences of emphasis between fanciers. For example some concentrate more on markings, others on type. Some of the rarest of the Rare Breeds will need a specialist judge.

• The list of breed classes. This will vary from show to show, depending on which breeds are popular locally. At the larger shows there will be classes for almost everything, but even then there will be some *Any Other Variety* (AOV) and *Any Other Colour* (AOC) classes. AOV classes are for breeds not expected in any great numbers. There will be one or two, depending on whether males and females are together or separate, at the end of each section, eg, AOV Light Breed, AOV True Bantam, etc. AOC classes are for rarer colours of popular breeds, e.g.

| White Leghorn M | Brown Leghorn M/F |
| White Leghorn F | AOC Leghorn M/F |

• When filling up the entry form allow one line per bird, even if you are entering two or more in one class. In the *Description* column write (from the example above) *Buff Leghorn Female,* for the *AOC Leghorn* class might be divided by the secretary if a lot more Leghorns are entered than usual. If everyone just writes *AOC Leghorn* the secretary will have to leave the class as it is.

• Read the schedule carefully! One common and embarrassing mistake is to enter (for example) a large Orpington in the Orpington bantam class or vice-versa. If this does happen, all is not lost. Tell the secretary, for there will probably be one or two spare cages in the hall, and the judge's forms can be amended.

• Some shows keep all classes as listed, even if there are only one or two entries. Other shows will 'amalgamate' classes. If, for example, yours was the only Brahma bantam entered, you may find it has been moved to *AOV Heavy Breed* when you arrive at the show. Each show clearly states their policy on classes in the 'Show Rules' in the Schedule.

# Show bird preparation

For full details of this there is a special book on the subject (*Managing Poultry for Exhibition* by H.Easom Smith), and the subject is also covered in the more comprehensive bantam books.

If your birds have been properly housed and managed since they were chicks they will not need too much in the way of beauty treatment, just concentrate on feet and faces. White or other light coloured birds and those with feathered feet will need a complete bath. If you are going to several shows, one complete bath will do for a couple of months.

## Shanks and feet

First wash them. Normal soap and water will usually do. If really dirty have some old fashioned (powder) *Ajax* or *Vim* handy. White and yellow feet show ingrained dirt under the edges of the scales, lines like dirty fingernails many times over. Gently remove this, as you would with dirty fingernails, using plastic cocktail sticks. Old birds naturally moult their scales, like reptiles. Old scales can sometimes be flicked off with a cocktail stick to make an old bird look better. Beginners should ask an experienced breeder to show them how to identify 'dead' scales as it is obviously cruel to try to remove a 'live' scale. Finish with a smear of *Vaseline*.

## Combs, wattles and lobes

Again, first wash the head, taking care not to get soap in their eyes. Gently dry them, initially with a towel, finishing off with paper kitchen-towel. Most fanciers keep their old, worn-out hand and bath towels as their 'chicken towels'.

White ear lobes and the whole face on Spanish are gently baby powdered. Combs, wattles and red ear lobes are smeared with baby oil. The oiling is best done on the morning of the show. Some exhibitors have their own recipes for 'head dressing', often including surgical spirit in the ingredients.

## Complete baths

When a bath is necessary, do it 5 to 7 days before the show and have a very clean cage to keep each bird in until the big day. Bird bathing is normally done in the kitchen sink, so first clear the decks in case they flap about or escape and send your crockery flying. Half fill the sink with warm, not too hot water and soak the bird (having washed the feet first). Gently wash the bird using either washing-up liquid, normal shampoo, baby shampoo or dog shampoo. Very dirty parts, foot feathers for example might need *Ajax* or *Vim*. Always rub in the direction the feathers grow or you will break feathers and do more harm than good.

Ready for the show! (Katie Thear)

After rinsing, apply hair conditioner and hold your soggy bird for a few minutes, then rinse again. At all stages keep their heads above water.

To dry, first wrap the bird in a towel, then stand it in a clean cardboard box for a few minutes for loose water to run off. Then, dry the bird thoroughly with a hair dryer on its medium heat setting, again in the direction the feathers grow. Bantam bathing is best done in the evening, so the dried bird can spend the night in a clean, dry box with wood shavings, near a radiator in your house. Beginners might like to try all this on any dirty bird they have before they do it for real on their potential champions.

## Helping at the show

Those orderly ranks of show cages do not appear by magic. All the hard work of setting up, usually the evening before the show, is done by a few keen supporters of each club. If the show is reasonably close, and if your bird preparation has been completed, any help will be very much appreciated. At the end of the show, if you can help take the cages down, this will also be very welcome. This is a dirty job, so dress appropriately.

When you get home it is a good idea to spray all your birds, in case they picked up any lice or mites at the show.

# Judging

Do not approach the judges while they are judging, but when they have finished they normally stay to explain their decisions to any puzzled or upset exhibitors.

As the prize cards are put up during the course of judging, most clubs put the *First Prize* cards up back to front. This is so the judges do not see the names when they are choosing the section winners (*Best True Bantam*, etc) and *Show Champion*. Some clubs go further, not putting the *First Prize* cards up until all the champions have been chosen.

## Becoming a judge

Not all successful exhibitors of long standing want to become regular judges, although even the reluctant judges will occasionally officiate at their breed club's specialised events. The breed clubs are allowed, under Poultry Club Rules to appoint anyone they want at their Club Shows, but most judging is done by judges who have passed PCGB tests. The tests follow the breed sections, *Hard Feather* test, etc, and candidates are only allowed to take one test per year.

Panel A judges have the whole set. Panel B have four or more certificates and Panel C have passed 1,2 or 3 tests. The tests consist of a practical and a written part and are taken at the National and Stafford Shows.

Most people start by taking the test which includes the breeds they keep themselves, and many are content to leave it at that, or perhaps do just one or two more. For example, many breeders will just do the tests for *Heavy Breeds*, *Light Breeds* and *True Bantams* as they are not that interested in *Hard Feather*, *Rare Breeds* or *Waterfowl*. However, even they should have some basic knowledge of the breeds in which they are not very interested as they will be involved, with other judges, in choosing *Show Champion* at the end of every show.

It is sensible to wait until you have been showing with some successes for five years or so before you take any tests. Meanwhile, volunteer as a judge's steward or assistant as often as possible, and also do a lot of background reading.

Left: Bantam eggs at The Royal Show, 2002.
Above: Championship Row at the National Show.
(Katie Thear)

# Health

*Most, but not all, poultry diseases can be avoided if the stock is kept under proper conditions.* (D.F. Suttie, 1929)

## Non-veterinary

There are some procedures that happen on a regular basis and which do not involve asking the vet for advice, unless there is a specific problem associated with them.

### Moulting

The natural process of dropping old feathers and the growing of new ones can be alarming to new poultry keepers. To start with, novices may think their half grown youngsters of some patterned varieties are completely wrong as juvenile plumage is often very different from the mature pattern expected.

Once mature, they will normally moult every year, starting in late summer. The whole process will take about twelve weeks, and hens will not lay (well, perhaps just the odd egg) while they are moulting. Broody hens with chicks usually moult while they are rearing the chicks. The combs shrink a little when moulting and grow back again towards the end of the process. Breeds with large single combs, such as Leghorns, Minorcas and Spanish have much more dramatic comb shrinkage, and look as if they must be ill, but don't worry, this is normal and those combs will soon be back as they should be.

Growing a new coat of feathers is just as nutritionally demanding as laying, perhaps more so. So ensure that the birds get the best of food, and as much as they want while they are moulting. Dietary supplements are also available.

### Wing clipping

This is the traditional method of curbing any persistent escapologists. Using a strong pair of scissors, cut off the primary (outer) set of flight feathers (except for the outer two) on *one wing only!* This puts the bird off balance when it tries to fly. Bear in mind that clipped birds cannot be entered in shows. Remember to re-clip persistent offenders after the moult. If your run fences are high enough, wing clipping should not be necessary.

### Nail clipping

Check all adult birds occasionally for overgrown claws. They can get very overgrown and even curl round. Use nail clippers to trim them back to a proper length. If you hold the claw up to the light you can usually see how far along the blood vessels go. Cut just beyond.

## Veterinary advice

Unfortunately, at some time in the future, your bantams may catch a disease and the services of a vet will be needed. Long before anything happens, it is a good idea to find out which practices in your area are best with poultry. Some city vets may be a bit rusty on hens and are unlikely to have the right drugs in stock.

Call outs are expensive and may sometimes be unnecessary. Take a couple of 'typical' sick birds to the surgery, and tell the vet how many birds you have in all. If necessary, the vet can arrange to have further investigations, such as blood tests or post-mortem examinations, carried out.

If the birds are healthy, well fed and well housed they are less likely to succumb to any infections. Fresh and clean drinking water is critical. The old saying is: *"Do not expect your livestock to drink water you wouldn't drink yourself."* Yes, I know hens will often drink from disgusting, muddy puddles, but this is something to be avoided, not an indication of dirty water being acceptable.

Poultry vaccines are designed for commercial use, and most only come in bottles of 1,000 doses, so are not generally a viable option for hobbyists, although poultry clubs could arrange for their members to share a combined order. Some vaccines are relatively inexpensive so wastage may be acceptable.

The vaccines that are most commonly given are for Marek's disease, Newcastle disease and Infectious bronchitis. There are a few large scale producers of pure breed large fowl who sell vaccinated birds, but virtually none supply bantams in this way.

## Coccidiosis

There are several types of this intestinal disease, each caused by a different species of Coccidial protozoan organism which causes bleeding in the intestine walls. *Eimeria tenella* is the most common and the most serious of this nasty group of bugs. It attacks chicks between three and ten weeks of age, and is often fatal. The chicks look generally sick and huddled, much the same as they do for a host of other diseases. One more specific symptom is blood in the droppings.

Chick crumbs and grower's pellets contain Coccidiostats, drugs which normally protect against the disease. A very virulent strain of Coccidiosis or very infectious (dirty) conditions may overcome the Coccidiostat. Coccidia spores can remain dormant and survive for a very long time. They will be in the droppings of other poultry and wild birds, and will survive on that spot of ground long after the droppings have gone. All chick rearing pens, whether under heat lamps or with broodies must be as clean as possible. When growing bantams are first let outside they are particularly vulnerable.

## Marek's Disease (Fowl Paralysis)

There are several forms of this virally caused cancerous disease. The classic form affects the leg and wing nerves, often on one side of the bird only. Some bantams with resistance to the virus will limp a bit for a week or so and then recover, but they are a minority, for most it is fatal. Generally it is best to kill any affected birds so they are not spreading infection to the rest of the flock.

Vaccines are only available in 1,000 dose bottles. Once opened, the vaccine, which is given to chicks as they are removed from the incubator, must be used within four hours. This is not a viable option for most hobbyists, so we have to rely on natural resistance. There is a lot of variation in resistance between breeds, and between strains within breeds.

The virus can be in a bantam, but dormant, for months. Some sort of stress may trigger the onset of actual disease. Starting to lay is one especially frustrating sort of stress. Mixing together groups of birds, and the fighting which then follows until they sort out their 'pecking-order', is another. Showing can also set off Marek's disease, but this is much less likely if the birds are used to being handled and have had some practice sessions in show cages at home.

## External parasites (Lice & Mites)

This is one area of disease control which bantam keepers can do themselves, but sadly, often do not. I have seen far too many flocks of birds which were badly affected by one or more type of parasite. Mites are painful for the birds and can even prove fatal, so it is vital for all bantam keepers to regularly handle their birds and check for unwanted visitors.

**Lice** are relatively large, light brown coloured creatures which live on the birds, mainly around the vent and down to the belly. If you do not actually see the lice, their 'nests' of eggs are very obvious, greyish-white lumps built up around the bases of feathers. Your local pet shop will have a range of suitable sprays and powders to kill the lice. The products intended for pigeon and cage-bird keepers are the same as poultry sprays. Active lice are easily killed, but the eggs will probably not be affected by the spray, so you will have to spray all your birds several times over a few weeks to finally clear the infestation. You must assume that if you find lice on one bantam, all the others will have lice too.

**Mites** are much more serious as they are bloodsuckers. They are smaller then lice and vary in size and colour. They are small and black, or fatter and blood-red, depending on the time since their last meal! Broody hens are literally sitting targets and can be killed by mites, so it is vital to spray nests regularly. Northern Mite live on the bantams all the time, and like lice usually concentrate around the vent. Red Mite spend their days in cracks and crevices in the poultry houses, mostly in nest boxes and on or near the perches. They then hop on when lunch, in the shape of your bantams, arrives. Look out for black or grey deposits (mite droppings) in the house. Mite infestations are usually worse in the summer. If you start scratching yourself when you enter your poultry house you know you have a bad infestation. Avian mites cannot live on human blood, so they will soon die or drop off.

Louse powder does not kill mites, so sprays are needed. *Duramitex* (for pigeon lofts) is very good for spraying the houses, but must not be used on the birds themselves or even when the birds are shut in the house as the fumes are very strong. It is sold as a bottle of liquid which is diluted with water and applied in a small sprayer as sold at garden centres. Periodic creosoting of poultry houses kills mite as well as preserving timber, but it is essential to leave them to dry out completely for a few days, before allowing the birds to go back in.

**Scaly leg mite**. This microscopic mite burrows under the leg and foot scales causing a whitish encrustation to be formed. In bad cases it can lead to bleeding and lameness. Bantams can be seen pecking at their own legs, a sign that they are in pain. Feather legged breeds are more susceptible as the feathers growing out give a way in for the mites. Repeated applications of medication are needed to eliminate scaly leg, and badly affected birds may be clear, but permanently disfigured. The damage to the scales may be such that they never grow back as they were originally. Traditional treatments include dipping the bird's feet in paraffin or old engine oil (although the latter is toxic to poultry).

Most of today's fanciers will probably prefer to use surgical spirit. Either dip the feet or apply with cotton wool buds. *Benzyl benzoate* can be ordered from your local pharmacy. It is mainly used for human and animal skin conditions, and seems to clear up scaly leg on chickens as well. Being a creamy liquid, it is probably more soothing for your bantams, especially if they are badly affected and bleeding. A few days after the first application of whichever treatment is used, repeat, and continue to repeat until the scales are clearing up. Some of the encrustation can be gently removed with a cocktail stick. Don't pull them off otherwise the legs will bleed.

**Depluming and feather mites**. There are several species which can damage the plumage and feathers. Some types are visible on the underside of feathers, especially wing flights. Mite sprays will clear many types. If there are any skin encrustations, try the *Benzyl benzoate*. Check all birds regularly, especially around the head and neck.

## Internal parasites

**Common intestinal roundworms**. These are the most frequently encountered and most easily cured type. *Piperazine* based treatments are available from vets and some farm and smallholder supply centres. Weight loss is the main symptom. Routine treatment, twice a year, is a good idea to clear any low level infestation. *Flubenvet* in the feed is also effective.

**Gapeworm**. These live in the trachea of fowls, turkeys, pheasants, etc. Affected birds have trouble breathing. These symptoms may be confused with other respiratory diseases, and whichever disease is present, a vet will be needed to identify the disease and supply the remedy. Again, *Flubenvet* in the feed is effective.

Nests of lice eggs adhering to the base of the feathers. (Katie Thear)

Scales pushed up on the legs showing the presence of scaly leg mites. (Katie Thear)

# Glossary   *Some Poultry Terms Explained*

**AOC**  Any or all other colours, as in a breed.

**AOV**  Any, or all other varieties, as in a breed.

**Autosexing breed**  Produces identifiable sexes at hatch from plumage barring.

**Barring**  Sharp black and white stripes across the feathers. Contrast this with 'cuckoo barring' which is wider and fuzzier.

**Beard**  Some breeds have a beard of feathers under the beak, ideally in a 'trilobed form'. On bearded birds the fleshy wattles are very small or entirely absent.

**Blocky**  Heavy bodied build, but with a fair length of back, eg, Sussex and Rhode Island Reds. Compare with 'cobby' below.

**Booted**  Apart from being the name of a Rare Breed, this is an old fashioned term for feather footed birds generally.

**Boule**  A swept back feather formation on the necks of Belgian bantams and Orloffs.

**Brassiness**  Yellowish colour which develops on the necks and backs of white birds, especially cocks, if allowed outside all summer. White birds, including mostly white birds like Silver Laced, intended for showing must be kept in the shade to avoid this. If you have a brassy bird which you would like to show, it will have to wait until after it moults and gets a new set of snow-white feathers.

**Breed**  Each breed is defined by its standard for body shape, comb type, ideal carriage, etc. Within a breed there will often be both large and bantam versions, each in several colour varieties.

**Carriage**  The ideal pose for a breed. Modern Game, a long legged, slim breed should stand tall and upright. Pekins are the reverse, having a characteristic 'tilt', with the tail higher then the head. Keen exhibitors will sometimes train their best birds to encourage them to stand properly. Modern Game breeders often use hook-on food pots, quite high up the pen netting and would never throw corn on the pen floor.

**Chick**  Young bird of either sex, up to the age of six weeks.

**Chicken**  Strictly speaking this only applies to young birds, under a year old.

**Cobby**  Short backed with a rounded body, eg, Wyandottes.

**Cock**  A male bird after its first adult moult (about 18 months old+).

**Cockerel**  A male bird younger than a cock.

**Cockerel-breeder** or Cock-breeder. See Double Mating.

**Comb**  The fleshy structure on top of a fowl's head. The normal serrated edged type is a Single comb. Other include: Rose, Pea (or Triple), Walnut, Horned and Cup.

**Condition**  State of bird in relation to health, cleanliness and appearance.

**Coverts**  Covering feathers on tail and wings.

**Crest**  Tuft of feathers on the head. Vary from very large ball shaped form on Polands to much more modest 'Tassels' on Sulmtalers.

**Cross breeding**  Mating of two birds of different breeds.

**Crow-headed**  Narrow, shallow head and beak

**Cuckoo**  See Barring

**Cushion** The thick plumage on the backs of some breeds (e.g.Orpingtons, Pekins and Wyandottes). A serious fault on those breeds which are required to have a slim, sleek outline. Also the lower back of the female.

**Cushion-comb** An almost circular, compact type of comb seen on Silkies.

**Double Comb** Old fashioned term for Rose comb.

**Double Laced** Plumage pattern of Barnevelders and Indian Game.

**Double Mating** Most of the breed standards were drawn up before the age of genetics. Breeders soon discovered they could not produce perfect males and females from one strain. Their way of producing show winners was to develop separate 'cock-breeder' and 'pullet-breeder' strains. Many of these varieties have complicated plumage patterns. For example, in Partridge Wyandottes a 'pullet breeder' cock (with a black and brown mixed colour breast) is needed to produce well marked females. Exhibition Partridge Wyandotte cocks (with a solid black breast) are bred from very fuzzy marked (cock breeder) hens. In Germany these have been officially separated into two distinct varieties. Many beginners make the mistake of thinking a 'pullet breeder' cock will produce only pullets.

**Duck footed** A disqualifying fault on bantams. It does *not* mean they have webbed feet! It does mean that one or both rear toes are permanently round the side of the foot instead of pointing back. Such a bird could easily lose balance and fall over. Historically this was a fatal flaw in a Game-cock.

**Duckwing** The traditional name for the silver version of the Black-red/partridge pattern. The wing bar (green on Black-red cocks) is shiny blue on Duckwing cocks, like the wing patch on a wild Mallard drake, hence the name.

**Ear-Lobes** The patch of skin below the holes which are the real ears. Many are red, the same colour as the surrounding skin, but many have very distinct white lobes. In almost all cases ear-lobe colour is related to egg shell colour; white lobed birds lay white shelled eggs while red lobed birds lay tinted or brown eggs.

**Feather-legged** Having feathers on the shanks and feet.

**Flock mating** Allowing several males to run with females in the flock.

**Foxy** A show fault, a reddish area on the wings of Partridge (as on Dutch and OEG), Duckwing and Pile females.

**Frizzled** Feathers which curl out from the body. The main feature on the Frizzle breed and Frizzled Japanese bantams. It can occur in a small way on other breeds where it is a fault associated with poor feather condition, often seen on Rhode Island Reds and in the necks of the cocks of many breeds. A wash followed by application of a good hair conditioner helps smooth out the feathers.

**Furnished** A mature cockerel, with its full set of tail and other feathering, is said to be 'fully furnished'.

**Gay** Not what you think! In fact it is excess white in the plumage of white spotted birds. Anconas usually have very neat little white spots in their first adult year, but go progressively more 'gay' in subsequent years, appearing nearly all white by the time they are four or five years old.

**Ground colour** Main plumage colour on which markings are applied, eg, White is the ground colour of Light Sussex and Silver Laced Wyandottes.

**Grower** Young bird between 6 weeks and maturity.

**Gypsy face** Dark (purple or maroon) skin colour required on some varieties.

**Hackles** Long, narrow pointed feathers on the neck of both cocks and hens and the backs of cocks (except 'henny cocks'- see below).

**Hangers** The lesser sickle feathers on the side of a cock's tail. Saddle hackle feathers are also sometimes called hangers, especially on Yokohamas and Sumatras where they are very long.

**Hard feathered** Tight close feathering, a feature of game birds.

**Hen** Female after the first adult moult.

**Henny or hen feathered cocks** A male bird with female type (and pattern, where applicable) plumage. They do not have normal male saddle hackles or tail sickles. It is characteristic of Sebrights and often seen on pullet breeder Pencilled Hamburgh males. It is caused by a gene which affects the hormones in the skin. It has no effect on fertility.

**In-breeding** Mating closely related birds

**Keel** Breastbone

**Lacing** Pattern on plumage where outside edge of a feather is of a different colour or shade from the rest. It may be single or double. See Double Laced.

**Leader** The pointed part, or 'spike' at the back of a rose comb.

**Leaf comb** Broad 'leaf' shaped comb, as in Houdan

**Lopped comb** Falling over to one side of the head. The large single combs on the females of Leghorns and some other breeds should be lopped. It is often a fault on other comb types.

**Mealy** Fine white stippling in the plumage. A fault on buff and black breeds.

**Mossy** Faulty markings, especially on laced breeds. Here it refers to any markings in the feather centres, which should be clear silver or gold. The term can also be applied to poorly marked specimens of other breeds where instead of having the precise pattern required, you have a fuzzy mess.

**Mottling** White tipping on the ends of feathers, as in Ancona.

**Muff or muffling**. Alternative name for beard.

**Mulberry** One version of 'Gypsy face'.

**Out-breeding** Mating different strains of the same breed.

**Pea comb** Also called 'Triple comb'. Resembles three small single combs fused together. The 'pea' name comes from its alleged resemblance to an open pod of peas. Seen on Brahmas, Indian Game and other breeds of Asian origin.

**Pearl eyed** Where the iris of the eyes are very light. Also called 'daw eyed'. Required on Malays, Ko-Shamo and some others, but a disqualifying fault on most other breeds.

**Pencilling** Generally fine markings on a feather. Be aware that the pencilling required on a Pencilled Hamburgh is completely different from that of a Pencilled Wyandotte.

**Peppering** Random fine markings. The back of a Gold Dutch female should be peppered, fine black spots on a brown ground colour. Here any tendency to any form of pencilling would be a serious fault.

**Primaries** The ten flight feathers of the wing. Also called 'flights'.

**Pullet** A female fowl up to a year old, after which it is a hen.

**Pullet breeder** See Double Mating.

**Pile or Pyle** A colour variety in several breeds. Males have bright orange necks, backs and parts of the wings. The rest of the plumage is white. Females are also mostly white, except for yellow necks and salmon-pink breasts.

**Reachy** Tall and upright carriage as seen on Malays and Modern Game.

**Roach back** Humped back, a deformity. Malays are required to have a curved back, which is not the same.

**Rose comb** A broad comb tapering to a point, or 'leader' at the back. The top surface is covered with small points ('work'). They vary from breed to breed. A Wyandotte's rose comb is much closer to the skull than the higher Hamburgh type rose comb.

**Rust** See 'Foxy'.

**Saddle** Lower back of male, corresponding to 'cushion' in female.

**Sappiness** A yellow tinge in white plumage. May be caused by the sun (see 'Brassiness') or by too much grass or maize in the diet when moulting.

**Secondaries** Inner quill feathers of the wings

**Self colour** A bird of one single plumage colour, eg, White.

**Serrations** The 'sawtooth' points along the top of a single comb. They should be nice wide wedges, not narrow fingers.

**Shafty** Lighter coloured in the shafts (centre stem or quill part) than the rest of the feathers. This is highly desirable on Welsummer females which have light golden shafts, nicely setting off their other richer shades. On any Buff breed light shafts are a serious fault as the aim is for all parts to be one even shade.

**Sheen** Surface gloss on black plumage

**Sickles** The top pair of long curved feathers on the tail of a cock.

**Side sprig** An extra spike growing out of the side of a single comb. A disqualification.

**Single comb** Narrow thin comb surmounted by serrations.

**Soft feathered** Soft plumage type, found in birds other than game birds. It varies according to the breed. Orpingtons have very soft, profuse plumage. Leghorns are still classed as soft feathered, but the plumage is tighter - midway towards hard feathered.

**Spangling** Spots of different colours at the ends of the feathers, eg, Spangled Hamburghs.

**Split wing** When the wing is opened out, a split wing has a gap between the primary (outer) and secondary (inner) groups of flight feathers. This is a disqualification on all breeds except Ko-Shamo, Nankin-Shamo and Yamato Gunkei, where it is almost encouraged, being associated with the extremely scanty plumage required on these curious breeds from Japan. For other breeds do not be too quick to 'write-off' young birds with split wing as the narrower juvenile plumage may look like split wing, but they will often be alright when the adult plumage grows.

**Spur** The 'horn' growing out from the shank (lower leg) of males, and sometimes females.

**Squirrel tail** A tail which is held so high that it tends to touch the head. A disqualification, except for Japanese (Chabo) bantams.

**Strain** A carefully bred family of a variety. Specialist breeders may keep several strains of one variety distinct and separate for many years by careful breeding.

**Striping** The (usually black) markings down the centre of neck and saddle feathers on some plumage patterns.

**Tail feathers** On cock birds this applies strictly to the straight feathers underneath the sickles and side hangers.

**Tassel** A small type of feathered head crest, as seen on Sulmtaler bantam males.

**Trio** A male and two females. Trio classes at the shows do not usually have very large entries as not many breeders will have two perfectly matching females.

**Type** General breed characteristic shape of body, legs, neck, etc.

**Undercolour** Colour of the fluff and lower part of the feathers only visible when feathers are lifted. An important point in certain breeds, eg, Rhode Island Reds, Barred Plymouth Rocks and all buff breeds.

**Variety** eg, bantam Buffs and large Blacks are both varieties of the Orpington breed.

**Vulture hocks** Stiff feathers projecting down from the leg joints on some feather legged breeds.

**Walnut comb** Small fleshy lump type of comb seen on Kraienköppes, Orloffs and Malays. Also called 'strawberry' comb.

**Wattles** The two fleshy appendages hanging down below the beak of most breeds.

**Wing bar** The line of shiny (green or blue glossed) black feathers across the wings of some colour patterns.

**Wing bay** The triangular part of a folded wing on some male plumage patterns.

**Wing bow** The upper or shoulder part of the wing.

**Wry back** A deformity similar to 'Roach back'.

**Wry tail** Another deformity, where the tail is permanently held over to one side. Watch suspect birds carefully before condemning them, as bantams are living, moving birds and may hold their tail to one side occasionally. Definite wry tailed cockerels should be killed, preferably the pullets as well, If you decide to keep any wry tailed pullets as layers, be sure not to hatch their eggs.

# Reference section

**Suggested Reading List**

*British Poultry Standards.* Victoria Roberts. 5th edition 1997 (6th edition due 2007). Blackwell Science Ltd and the Poultry Club of Great Britain.
A complete description of all recognised varieties of large fowl, bantams, ducks, geese and turkeys. Equivalent books in other countries by their respective governing bodies.
*Starting with Chickens.* Katie Thear. 1999. Broad Leys Publishing Ltd.
Introduction to keeping chickens on a household scale, with comprehensive coverage of pure breeds and hybrids, and their management.
*Free-Range Poultry.* Katie Thear. 3rd edition. 2002. Whittet Books Ltd.
Comprehensive manual for commercial as well as household management of poultry.

**General bantam books** (in date order)
*Bantams.* Entwisle W.F. 1894 + modern reprints.
Entwisle created several varieties, described in this excellent book.
*The Bantam Fowl.* McGrew T.F. 1899 + modern reprint. USA.
*Bantams as a Hobby.* Proud P. 7 editions between 1901 and 1920. No modern reprints.
*The Bantams down to Date.* Shakespeare J, 1925. USA. No modern reprints.
*Bantams and Miniature Fowl.* Silk W.H. 1951+ newer editions revised by Dr.J.Batty.
*Bantams for Everyone.* Easom Smith H. 1967 + later editions
The various editions of Silk and Easom Smith are not currently in print but can often be found in second-hand/antiquarian bookshops and are well worth buying.
*Book of Bantams.* American Bantam Association, 1967, USA.
*Bantam Breeding and Genetics.* Jeffrey F.P. 1977. UK. (First published in 1974 in USA under title of *Bantam Chickens*). Most comprehensive bantam book.

**Single breed books**
There have been a surprisingly large number of these published over the last century or so in Britain, America and other countries, some having been produced by breed clubs.
*Japanese Bantams.* Banning-Vogelpoel A.C. 1983, American Bantam Association.
*Understanding Japanese Bantams.* Palin J.K. 1980 UK.
*Wyandotte Bantams.* Jeffrey F.P. 1984, American Bantam Association.
*The Wyandotte Manual.* Deickman G. circa 1964, Wyandotte Club of Australia.
*De Wyandotte.* Nederlandse Wyandotte Club. 1998. Limited edition in Dutch.
*Understanding Modern Game.* Batty Dr. J. & Bleazard J.P. 1976.
*Understanding Old English Game.* Batty Dr J. 1973.
*Understanding Indian Game.* Hawkey K.J.G. 1978.

**General poultry books**
These include sections on bantams, and much of the information on the large breeds is the same for their miniature versions.
*The Illustrated Book of Poultry.* Wright L. Several editions from 1872 to 1891
*The Book of Poultry.* Wright L. Several editions from 1885 to 1891
*The New Book of Poultry.* Wright L. Several editions from 1902 to 1911
*Wright's Book of Poultry.* Revised by S.H.Lewer. Several editions from 1912 to 1919
*Lewis Wright's Poultry 1983.* Batty Dr J. Includes reproductions of all the colour plates from the originals, together with an edited text.

*Encyclopaedia of Poultry.* Brown J.T. 2 vols. 1908. Also 1921 edition revised by J.S.Hicks
This pair of books can often be bought for under £50 from book dealers.
*Our Poultry and All About Them.* Weir H.W. 2 vols.1902.
*The Poultry Book.* Weir H.W. & 'many expert American breeders' 3 vols. 1905.
*The Poultry Book.* Wingfield W.W. & Johnson G. 1853.
*Feathered World, Poultry World* and *Poultry* magazine yearbooks published 1910-1939
*Stairway to the Breeds.* Kay I. 1997

## Technical books
*Commercial Chicken Production Manual.* North M. O. 1978, USA.
*Incubation: A Guide to Hatching & Rearing.* Thear Katie. 3rd edition 1997.
*The Incubation Book.* Anderson Brown. 1979
*Diseases of Free-Range Poultry.* Victoria Roberts. 2000. Whittet Books.

## Organisations
*Poultry Club of Great Britain.* Mike Clark, 30 Grosvenor Road, Frampton, Boston, Lincs PE20 1DB. Tel: 01205 724081
*National Federation of Poultry Clubs.* Adrian Keep. Tel: 01234 365150
*The Rare Poultry Society.* Richard Billson. Tel: 01162 593730 (evenings)

## Stock
When purchasing pure bred birds, make sure that they come from a reputable breeder. The Poultry Club can put you in touch with the relevant breed club. Also, *Country Smallholding* magazine has a Breeders' Directory in each issue. Tel: 01392 444274. Other publications carrying advertisements for stock include *Smallholder.* Tel: 01326 213333 and *Fancy Fowl.* Tel: 01728 685832.

## Housing
As bantams are small, many owners will utilise existing garden buildings or make their accommodation and runs. However there are suppliers of suitable poultry housing.
*The Domestic Fowl Trust.* Tel: 01386 833083. www.mywebpage.net/domestic-fowl-trust
*Fishers Poultry Houses.* Tel: 01302 841122. Email: smpltd@aol.com
*Forsham Cottage Arks.* Tel: 0800 163797. www.forshamcottagearks.co.uk
*Gardencraft.* Tel: 01766 513036. www.gcraft.co.uk
*Lindasgrove Arks.* Tel: 01283 761510
*Littleacre Products.* Tel: 01543 481312
*The Poultry Pen.* Tel: 01673 818776. www.poultrypen.co.uk

## Incubators
*Aliwal Incubators.* Tel/Fax: 01508 489328
*Brinsea Products Ltd.* Tel: 01934 823039. www.brinsea.com
*Curfew Incubators (SARL).* Tel: 01621 741923. www.curfewincubators.com
*Interhatch.* Tel: 0114 255 2340
*MS Incubators.* Tel: 0116 247 8355/07788 661564
*Southern Aviaries.* Tel: 01825 830930 Fax: 01825 830241

## Mail Order Equipment Suppliers
*Ascott Smallholding Supplies.* Tel: 0845 130 6285. www.ascott-shop.co.uk
*Cyril Bason.* Tel: 01588 673204/5
*The Domestic Fowl Trust* - see housing
*Oxmoor Smallholder Supplies.* Tel: 01757 288186
*Solway Feeders Ltd.* Tel: 01557 500253. www.solwayfeeders.com
*SPR Greenfields Farm.* Tel: 01243 542815. www.sprcentre.co.uk

# Index